Non Famous People

William J. Bozic, Jr.

DEDICATION

To my family and to all of the non-famous people out there.

CONTENTS

INTRODUCTION

Dystopian novels and romantic stories involving supernatural creatures are very popular among teens and adults but perhaps the market is saturated, so my thought for this book was to create a whimsical young adult drama written as a first-person narrative from the perspective of a teacher or coach.

Jay Asher's style of first person narrative in *13 Reasons Why*, Laurie Halse Anderson's *Twisted*, Chris Crutcher's *Staying Fat for Sarah Byrnes* and Elizabeth Laband's *The Tragedy Paper* served as the impetus for this approach. Each chapter is a short story about fictitious people in somewhat realistic situations taking place at various public secondary schools around the United States.

Every short story in this book is entirely fiction but done in a realistic way so if anyone is led to believe they know any of the people or schools, they are entirely incorrect because everything is absolutely fictitious. The Family Educational Rights and Privacy Act (FERPA) (20 U.S.C. § 1232g; 34 CFR Part 99) is a Federal law that protects the privacy of student education records, therefore any connection must be considered entirely coincidence.

The title of this book, Non Famous People, is a reflection on the value of every special individual who will never receive any recognition, yet stays in the memory. Probably some readers will be drawn to their own life experiences in which they interacted with extraordinary people who were worthy of a full-length motion picture, yet barely linger in the memory. It is to these people in everyone's memory, and my family, that this book is dedicated.

1 CHICAGO CATSUP KID

The school bond which had been passed decades ago finally resulted in the much-needed renovation of a school built in the open school concept. As renovations took place a ninth-grade campus was created out of portable buildings in what had been fields used for sports. Beyond the portable campus were old subdivisions and new apartment buildings. My portable had once been used by elementary schools so it had toilets inside but these had been closed and rendered inoperable.

When the Chicago Catsup Kid first came to my portable about midyear, I sensed something was terribly wrong. His skin was dirty, his hair looked like it had not been shampooed in a long time – but I really couldn't tell because dirty hair and ripped-up clothes day after day was in style and called the "Distressed Look". I probably could've contacted Child Protective Services for neglect, but he was just like almost all the other kids so he didn't stand out too much.

The Chicago Catsup Kid entered my classroom and seemed to be excited to get attention. He spoke a lot about any topic, particularly his love for being at our school. The Chicago Catsup Kid started to drop off from attending my seventh period class, so I called home. In those days the attendance office should have caught all of the absences and contacted the home, but waiting for the attendance office would be like waiting for a pot of gold at the end of a rainbow to appear at one's feet, so I felt it was best to call to find out what was happening. I reached the Chicago Catsup Kid's grandfather, who told me his grandson had come from Chicago and that he was an old man trying to take care of a teenage boy and really wasn't physically up to the task. He was working two jobs and elderly so he just was doing the best that he could. The grandfather was surprised his grandson was not attending class and kind of didn't believe me.

At the same time I called the Chicago Catsup Kid's grandfather, I made a call to another parent about their son's lack of attendance. The father was very rough and I sensed he was an angry drunk by the tone of his voice and the very harsh comments and threats he made to me for calling him. Little did I realize the connection between these two troubled boys...

Although I never suspected because they did not show any comradeship in class, the Chicago Catsup Kid would sneak out of school alone to play video games and goof around while his grandpa was not home. It did not take long for the Chicago Catsup Kid to become bored around the house so he invited the aforementioned boy to go with him. At first they would play video games instead of coming to my seventh period World Geography class, but later they decided they needed more gaming time so they skipped more classes. Eventually they just didn't even show up to school. Gaming all the time eventually got a little bit boring so they graduated to more mischief.

Both boys decided they would go to the local supermarket and raise Cain. Yes, you can guess the Chicago Catsup Kid's favorite thing to smash and dash at the supermarket. At first the boys would sneak up on the catsup and smash the bottles on the floor then hide around the corner while employees came to fix up the mass destruction and wonder how it had occurred. Swiftly the supermarket employees smelled foul play. The boys became more brazen, and rather than smashing the bottles on the floor, they would throw the bottles and watch the glass and catsup fly everywhere. When the supermarket started to put a lookout and be on the high alert for catsup crimes, they switched to other products which would cause a mess when thrown when smashed across the aisles of the supermarket, but their true love was catsup.

It didn't take long for an "All-Points Bulletin" to be placed on the two boys by the supermarket. The supermarket even managed to get their photos and post them near the manager's office in order for every employee to take notice. For that particular supermarket these guys were Public Enemies #1. The boys began to sneak into the supermarket with crowds and do their dirty deeds, then run as fast as they could while being chased by supermarket employees. I even managed to see the "wanted posters" for my two students whom I had not seen in months- their appearance had not changed a bit.

Eventually the school attendance office noticed the boys were truant much too frequently, and although the school never put it together that the two were in tandem for their truancy, the assistant principal was pressed to take some action. Both boys were sent to the Alternative Learning Center. I saw the Chicago Catsup Kid roaming on the grounds of the portable campus a year or two later and he said he dropped out and really regretted not being in our school, because apparently it was boring to do anything else and he was extremely unwelcome at the local supermarket.

2 CIGARETTE

Cigarette was a short boy who weighed a little over 100 pounds in the ninth grade. Cigarette had a flat top haircut, bulging eyes, and always seem to be hungry for both food and attention.

Cigarette would frequently interrupt class with attempts at comedy. In the beginning of the school year most of the kids would laugh, but by midterm, his attempts at humor fell on deaf ears. Teachers made telephone calls to Cigarette's mother who was living alone with only her beloved child for whom she'd doted on in the extreme. Every day Cigarette's mother claimed that she hand-made hamburgers and filled a tall glass of milk for Cigarette to enjoy as soon as he entered their door so he could get enough energy to make it through his studies, watch TV, and play games, until she made dinner for him.

Cigarette announced to the class, and his mother unsolicitedly volunteered in a phone call, that Cigarette once was scolded by an English teacher for using the word "ain't" so the mother found the word in the dictionary, because "ain't actually is in the dictionary", she proceeded to get teacher fired. How? The teacher made a typo on some assignment, because, by her reasoning a professional educator should never say any criticism to her child if they were not perfect themselves. The teacher paid dearly for his typo and lost his job. I thought, "Ain't that a shame…"

Cigarette's mother went on a rant about all of the teachers at the school and how incompetent they were. Cigarette's mother could not comprehend that her child was anything but an angel sent from heaven, and she neglected to comprehend that the teachers who were calling were actually doing their job to try to work with her on her son's behavior and his academic improvement.

Cigarette's mother announced that all the teachers were being so rough on her dear child that he confided to her that he was having to go to the bathroom frequently because it was affecting his bowels, so she got a bathroom pass from the school nurse, which would allow Cigarette to depart at will from any class at any time of his choosing.

Cigarette would make jokes about parties and getting away with almost anything. Some of his pals in turn poked fun at Cigarette about how he manipulated his mother and his crazy diet of hamburgers and milk because apparently some of his pals visited their home and the mother force-fed his acquaintances with hamburgers and milk. Cigarette retorted angrily to every comment in defense of his saint-like mother, but eventually put his foot down so his mother was ordered not to continue with the mandatory feedings of hamburgers and milk to every visitor.

Cigarette would come and go to class as he pleased, and to be honest, most teachers were happy to see him gone because his constant attention-seeking outbursts, sarcasm, and mockery disrupted class instruction. It was not for us to judge if he had irritable bowels, but he did tend to spend an inordinate amount of time in the bathrooms. Can you say "Lactose Intolerance"?

Some of the teachers noticed an unmistakable odor of tobacco around Cigarette and his friends. He flaunted lots of cash in small denominations. Cigarette apparently was carrying packs of; you guessed it, cigarettes and selling these in the bathroom for a dollar apiece. If there are 20 cigarettes in a package then you can do the math!

Cigarette's business lasted for about four years until he left for the Marine Corps. Given the fact that his mother was extremely overprotective, we can only surmise what a shock to his system that life was like for him at United States Marine Corps basic training…

3 DENISE THE MENACE

Denise the Menace was the kind of student who knew which buttons to push to get me riled and pushed them regularly. One day Denise the Menace decided to sit in another student's seat and so that student had to move to another seat so eventually the class seating chart was completely confounded. Given that some students had vision issues or other individual educational issues requiring preferential seating, this was like throwing spaghetti up into the air and trying to connect the noodles back on to the plate. The instigator was Denise the Menace, and we all had a good laugh, but when it came time to good-naturedly put everybody back in order Denise the Menace flatly refused and flew into a rage about being singled out.

Our principal was the kind of administrator who would make statements like "The students come first" and "We are all here for the kids", which he and all the teachers generally believed, because face it, why are teachers in education? Why do we have schools if not to help the students? With this kind of logic, the principal believed that if any student complained about a teacher that teacher should shortly lose his or her job- Due process be damned.

Invariably I was called out of class and asked some very open ended questions intended to trap me into incriminating myself. I was absolutely incredulous as to the line of questioning and begged permission to ask who might be accusing me of such unteacher-like, unprofessional behavior so I could properly respond and clear my name. The principal refused to even give me an inkling of who might have accused me of all these childish behaviors, saying that he wanted to protect the student from retribution. The principle's daughter was in my classroom and seemed to like me and we never had an issue so I was left to ponder, but not for long.

Denise the Menace strutted into my classroom with a grin from ear to ear telling me that she was going to get me fired and that I better start looking for another job somewhere else outside of teaching. Pointedly she joyfully exposed that she would make it her duty to see that wherever else I worked she would make my life miserable, especially if I worked as a waiter, because she would have me run for her trifles and leave no tip.

I called the home phone of Denise the Menace, but got voicemails and left messages to please call me back. No calls back were returned, so as a last resort I called the mother at her work. The mother was frosty with me to say the least because she worked at a shipping company and really didn't have any extra time to spare. I tried to explain as quickly as possible that I was concerned about her daughter's behavior and the threats made against my job, but that it would never influence my behavior towards her daughter. Denise the Menace's mother replied that both my voice, tone, and word choices reminded her of Denise the Menace's father, whom she was divorcing because he was a

(a blue streak full of expletives) then hung up the phone.
It appears I drew the bad straw of being similar to her father, whom Denise the Menace and her mother despised. For a moment I wondered about the poor man, but then I had to figure out quickly what could be done with the cards stacked against me as the noose tightened around my neck with the proverbial tall branch and short string attached to it. The principal who always praised my work abruptly did an about face and put me on his "bad teacher- soon to be fired" list. The principal believed teachers should stay employed only if they were popular with all students, so he would have great ratings for his school and himself. The principal forgot that even multi-million dollar sluggers in Major League Baseball do not hit a homerun at every at bat, yet this is what he fantasized for the institution while he was the manager.

Denise the Menace was wise enough to not do anything serious, but she continued unabated with every sort of little misbehavior she could think of: talking while I was talking, making sarcastic remarks, not doing her work, inciting others, etc. The other students were cognizant of the game she was playing and one by one refused to join along. Pretty soon she was the single person in the room misbehaving and the other students were tired of putting up with her games. Peer pressure took a toll on her. When the tide turned against her, Denise the Menace was given a schedule change and would no longer be my student. I was all too happy to sign a statement that there were irreconcilable differences even though it was not necessarily the truth.

The principal called me to his office and read me the riot act. I explained to the principal that his own daughter was in one of my classes and if there was any hint of any malfeasance he should contact his daughter. Of course it was well-known the principal's daughter reported to him regularly about all of her teachers. I also explained that somehow I was similar to the father she detested so the student was lashing out in an attempt to release her frustrations against her father.

As the time grew near for contract renewals and another large percentage of the staff prepared to pack their bags, because "you can't please all of the people all of the time", like a ray of light through dark clouds, we received the news that the principal would not be returning. No reason was given for his departure. Perhaps it was due to his unprofessional tactics, uncomfortable Gestapo "Gotcha" approach which kept teachers nervous, and high attrition rate for staff? As an added piece of irony the principal's attractive wife and daughter left him, too.

Lesson:
Happy Teachers= Happy Students,
Happy Students= Happy Parents,
Happy Parents= Happy School Board Members,
Happy School Board Members = Happy Administrators.

4 DOG BOY

Dog Boy brought his skateboard to school and would skateboard through the walkways of the ninth grade portable campus. Teachers would tell him to stop but he would just continue with his skateboarding. Other students enjoyed watching him try to do tricks and fall on his face. Dog Boy was not a good skater, but he was the most outstanding dog I ever heard.

Dog Boy came from California. His father no longer wanted his company, so he was sent to live with his mother. Dog Boy really wanted to go back with his dad and felt that if he caused enough trouble his mother would send him back, but he didn't realize that every time he got into some sort of trouble, it made his father even less likely to want to take him back.

Dog Boy was in my portable and drew the attention of everyone when he put rock salt on top of the skateboard and began to inhale as if he was snorting cocaine. His eyes became solid bloody red and his already pale skin became even paler. I hit the emergency button and the nurse, police, counselors, and assistant principals arrived. Normally there would be a boatload of paperwork before anything would be done, but in this case it was so obvious the nurse immediately took him, followed by the police. I completed the proper documentation. Surprise, surprise, the mother tried to get me fired because I was supposedly "overreacting" but I didn't sweat it because based on what everyone experienced with Dog Boy her grievance against me didn't go very far.

Somehow, while Dog Boy was living in California with his largely absentee father, he perfected the sound of a dog. The campus police constantly saw him skateboarding and eventually they would catch them. Remember he was not a skater boy, so the cops would always see the boy later and eventually threatened to write citations. Dog Boy liked the fact that the police eventually decided to write citations because his mother would have to pay the fines since he was a minor and maybe he would be returned to his California dream. Boy's mother took the skateboard.

Dog Boy then decided to use his skills at mimicking the sound of a puppy dog by passing classrooms and mimicking the sound and then scurrying away. Teachers throughout the campus would hit the panic button, and exclaim that there was a dog loose in the school. It was believable because students had unleashed mice and squirrels on campus as pranks in the past. Some staff members would chase after the supposed dog and find nothing, almost as if it was a ghost dog or a dog with greyhound speed. Since Dog Boy was doing the dog sounds on campus instead of the outside portable classrooms it was just a matter of time for the police to figure out via cameras that Dog Boy was the culprit.

Dog Boy was admonished to stop barking or face serious consequences. I often wondered just how the police could write a citation for barking like a dog and what would happen in a courtroom.

5 FIREBUG

Once upon a time an absolutely brilliant plan was envisioned by some ex-military personnel to turn barren land in Florida into a place where retirees, or even active duty military personnel, could build their dream homes on 1/3 acre lots. The group bought a wide swath of land and laid out roads in a grid system with numbers and directions that stretched for miles. The roads were built narrow and with only a small amount of pavement. Prospective buyers would be driven out to a lot and sold the land at an affordable price where they could eventually build their Florida dream house in the sunshine. One by one, the trickle became a deluge of retirees, and in some cases their children, who built on top of these lots. As more and more people moved into this huge expanse of open flatland, the resulting construction vehicles and moving vans tore-up the roads so that it became a bit like an army obstacle course just to drive.

There was absolutely no city water, so each homeowner had to dig a septic tank and a water well into the brackish water beneath the surface, and then heavily treat the water to make it potable. The rumor was that the water was so bad it would be safer to drink straight Coca-Cola rather than water. Words like typhoid and dysentery were whispered and those selling water purification as well as medical professionals did a booming business.

The initial geniuses who hatched this plan probably did so with the kindest and most genuine intentions but as soon as legal action began they paid themselves huge bonuses which bankrupted the company and they left. Homeowners had no recourse and paving all the roads would be a gargantuan tax retirees living on fixed incomes could not afford to pay, so not much money went into fixing the situation and over time people grew to accept this flawed vision of their golden years.

These retirees felt they had done their fair share of paying for schools back home when they were younger, so school funding was not their obligation. The retires did not have any school aged children so out of self-interest and their own low incomes, school funding was their absolute lowest priority. The schools were made of cinder block and slapped together in a makeshift way. Even the school district headquarters was in an abandoned strip mall which was so substandard it was hard to imagine this was a functioning public building. The district realized it could hire the best teachers for the lowest amount of money because they would recruit in northern states in order to get older teachers who wanted to retire to the Florida good life, but still make a little extra income. The school district rationalized these quality, experienced teachers would really just be working for fun and to supplement their Social Security checks. Bill Nye-the Science Guy, didn't fit the mold for the school district because he was a young married teacher with a small family who was absolutely devoted to teaching. Bill Nye was the kind of guy who would stay up late at night after putting his children to bed just so he could create new and exciting lessons for his students. Bill Nye was adored by almost all of the people with whom he came in contact. Sometimes a great teacher like this attracts a telltale lone wolf intent on causing trouble, like the Firebug.

Bill Nye had irritated bowel syndrome, so his assignment was to a science room very close to a restroom. One day he bolted out of the classroom to get to the restroom, and, within a few minutes, his cinderblock cracker-jack box of a classroom went up in flames. I could see flames and smoke immediately ignite in his square, and before the fire alarm could even ring students were racing in a frenzied fashion to get outside and down the stairs to the ground where they moved like a pack of wild dogs towards the street in order to get away from the fire. In the chaos students were injured and teachers were unable to control their frightened students.

Although we had regular fire drills, the real thing brought out the true colors in all of the students. Everyone knows fire moves quickly and is a universal cause of fear among both man and beast, yet the rapidity of the flames, even in Bill Nye's cinderblock building, was profoundly astonishing. Fire officials will tell you never to go back to a burning building or to attempt to collect belongings, but unless you see the fury of a fire in action, those words of warning are not as impactful. Cement blocks do not burn, so it was beyond shocking how fast Bill Nye's room became an inferno of billowing smoke and fire.

The fire department darted to the school but had to negotiate the bad roads and heavy traffic. As the plumes of smoke filled the sky, frightened parents joined the traffic jam to get to the school to save their children. Amidst the fire, which was contained rather quickly, terrified parents were roaming into the parking lot asking anyone they could find about where their beloved teenaged child was located. The parents grew insanely belligerent when bewildered teachers could not exactly tell them where their child might be amongst 3000+ students and teachers in the melee. The administration also had to deal with increasingly hostile parents who wanted answers immediately and proper documentation to release students to various adults amidst the hornet's nest of smoke and chaos swirling in and around the school.

To make matters worse, some of the students decided it would be fun to go back into the school to watch the firefighters take care of the blaze. The students blatantly ignored the excoriations of the teachers to stay in their designated areas so the thrill-seeking kids went back into the fire zone, causing the fire department to allocate precious resources towards crowd control rather than fighting the fire. Police officers were trying in vain to deal with the traffic, so now the undermanned fire department who were awaiting support that was caught in traffic jams, had to deal with curious students who would not take no for an answer. Thankfully, the fire was quickly contained, but it took hours to return the school to normal. The community was outraged at what had transpired.

The one room science annex was completely out of commission, so schedules had to be redone and Bill Nye was under investigation, which at the end of the school year resulted in him not being rehired. Apparently, when he bolted to the restroom, a student turned on the gas valves and lit either a match or cigarette lighter which ignited the classroom. The other students thought it might be funny to burn down their school, so they were quickly out of the room before Firebug turned on all the gas valves of the science room. Surprisingly all of the students kept silent about the identity of the Firebug.

Across the street from the school there were those third of an acre lots and miles of grids of streets, which were totally uninhabited. Tallgrass, weeds, and who knows what from nature had reclaimed most of these lots so that it appeared to be a broad savanna rather than unbuilt housing development. One day, during an extremely breezy period of time, somehow, that area was lit on fire. Unlike the science room, this was a major inferno engulfing territory like a giant whirlwind of death. Dangerous critters of all shapes and sizes were running for their lives from the fire directly into the school area. Those students and teachers who had phobias of snakes and rats were absolutely livid. As fast as we possibly could think, people evacuated and ran in all directions away from the fire and critters. Unlike the previous incident, this time everybody was purely terrified to the core because there appeared to be no way out and the flames were like a swift moving wave of hot death. Even the few who were not impressed by the previous fire were left with a primal instinct to escape. The melancholy knowledge that there was no possible escape route caused people even to start to pray and reveal mistakes that they had made in some hopes of reconciliation and penance before their imminent doom.

As the scorching hot flames under the already blazing hot Florida sun approached the campus, the fire department managed to set up their engines in front of the school and blast at the flames like a headlong charge. Think of Pickett's Charge from the Battle of Gettysburg and you have a pretty good idea of the bravery and fortitude of the men and women in the fire department as they attacked headlong into a wall of flame. Thank God for super-duper chemicals! A barrier was laid that the flames just couldn't jump, so our lives and the school were saved.

While the initial line was created in front of the school, simultaneously the fire department attempted to envelop the fire. Traffic again became a problem but this time authorities managed to notice a car with a student parking permit from the high school on the other side of the fire. It didn't take long to figure out the same student was also one of Mr. Nye's science students.

The Firebug's initial plan was to extinguish the career of a popular teacher, but he discovered that he really liked fire and had a vengeance towards all public education, hence his second effort. The Firebug had some type of pyromania tendencies, and was obviously mentally disturbed, but it was decided the best place for him, other than burning him at the stake, would be a hardcore penitentiary for an excessive period of time where he might also receive mental health services.

Firebug probably would've been treated differently if it had not been for Fire Chief Rick. The fire chief believed he was the king of the county and no one was going to cross him, so there was absolutely no pity for Firebug. Fire Chief Rick was extremely brutal to anyone who did not immediately comply with any request that he made, even if the request was borderline ridiculous. Fire Chief Rick prided himself on making sure that every building was above and beyond the fire code so he took it as a personal affront that a public high school under his domain could catch fire and was draconian in his desire to go after Firebug who he perceived had sullied his reputation. Even the other fire chiefs thought that Fire Chief Rick was overbearing. In fact, that's how he got the nickname Fire Chief Rick or Fire Chief Richard, because this fire chief was considered to be a_____.

Fire Chief Rick went into a restaurant that was absolutely packed to capacity and ordered the hostess to put a table for himself and his entourage in front of the fire exit. The teenage girl who was serving as hostess told him she could not because it was a violation of the fire code to block the fire exit and also to go over the number of people allowed by law in the building. OMG, Fire Chief Rick let loose a string of curse words at the high school girl, which caused the new manager to come over. Fire Chief Rick let loose even more profanity and threats on the manager. Among them were closing down the restaurant, throwing everyone that was employed at the restaurant in jail, and fines for the owner. The manager of the restaurant complied, but refused to apologize and was even so bold as to say to Fire Chief Rick that he hoped Fire Chief Rick was pleased that he had made a little minimum wage teenage girl cry, whereupon Fire Chief Rick demanded free food and drinks for his entourage or else, due to the apparent rudeness of the new manager who should've known better. Fire Chief Rick got the meal and drinks complimentary and a long letter of apology from the owner, so one is left only to guess at how hotly Firebug was burnt when he was alone for "questioning" with Fire Chief Rick… Maybe prisons can keep dangerous people in, but some dangerous people are still on the outside…

6 HANNIBAL LECTOR

It was the last day of school and a counselor friend of mine asked me a favor to sit in on an Individual Educational Placement (IEP) meeting for a student with special needs.. Since it was the last day of school and teachers were running everywhere to take care of chores Ronald McDonald knew he was asking me to do him a big favor. Ronald McDonald had followed me through various schools over the years and was always very kind. Both of us came from Florida so we would often talk about our shared experiences in the Sunshine State. I knew Ronald was in a bind and could not help but offer assistance. Besides, IEP's usually only lasted about 30 minutes or so…

I met a woman who appeared to be a drug-induced mentally ill mother who had an attorney with her provided by some agency with a name I really can't remember. The bottom line was her son was special and she was going to attempt to find a way to sue the school district for not taking care of her dear son in an effort to become a rich lady and probably have money for more and better drugs. The attorney didn't seem to know much about education, but was anxious by her questions to find ways to obtain money or, in other words, create a lawsuit. The IEP lasted all day and long after the school day was finished. Eventually, in the evening, we adjourned.

The next day the IEP continued, but instead of a lawyer, there was a child advocate. The child advocate appeared to know something about schools and managed to delay the meeting by trying to obfuscate over technicalities to the point that the meeting lasted all day. By this time the school year had already ended, but the meeting terminated at the end of our normal contract time, even though none of us were being paid because the school year was over.

In the days before the coming school year all staff usually attend training sessions and get some time to make class preparations. Mr. Arrow and I were called into an special meeting, along with Ms. Christian, and some other teachers. A specialist from the district explained to us that we were going to have to take additional hours of unpaid training because we had a very special student. We were told this student was fixated on cars which at first delighted me because I also enjoy muscle cars.

Driving a Mustang along the beach with one palm on the wheel and keeping your foot over top of the break because you never needed to accelerate, rather you needed to hold the Mustang back ,was how I learned to drive. Years later we were taught to hold our hands 10 and 2 around the wheel at all times, but due to airbags in the steering wheel everyone is taught to place their hands at 9 and 3, otherwise when, and if, the airbag goes off your wrists and arms will be mangled by the very tool set up to keep you from getting hurt...

We were also told the student was obsessed with "Pokémon", which began to make me wonder and get a little uneasy. The final straw of my uneasiness came when we were told the student was extremely obsessed with "Hot Rocks". I tried to keep a straight face and wondered what the heck "Hot Rocks" was? I knew if my wife caught me Googling "Hot Rocks" on our home computer, I'd have a lot of precarious explaining to do, but if I googled it at work I'd certainly be fired, so I took the risk at home. OMG was I in for an unpleasant voyage.

Oh, and the most important quirk, was the student's desire for the taste of human flesh.

When Hannibal Lecter appeared in my classroom I was prepared by getting some hot rod magazines in order to reward him for positive behavior. Ms. Christian was especially appreciative of this step because he had already started to bite her. Ms. Christian believed that Hannibal Lecter was indeed possessed by the Devil. Unfortunately for Ms. Christian, every attempt to have the student removed from the regular classroom failed. Ms. Christian was bitten multiple times, and began wearing armed guards and leg guards, similar to those worn for police K-9 training. Ms. Christian didn't have the money to sue and since she was a paraprofessional she had really no one to stand up for her.

Hannibal Lecter had issues, but he was a reasonably intelligent student. Mr. Arrow and I used whatever we could and strategic seating arrangements near the door to successfully keep him in check, but some other teachers weren't so lucky. Hannibal Lecter escaped their rooms and chased after people to chomp-on in the hallway like a wild, rabid dog chasing prey. Usually we worry about violent kids flipping people, rather than eating people, but this kid had an insatiable appetite for human flesh and saw any pretext as an opportunity to devour innocent people in he perceived as the human buffet of our school. To make matters worse, any time an assistant principal or anyone on staff attempted to detain him and news reached the mother, she filed preposterous lawsuits which frustrated the district's legal team and accountants because they had to deal with even more hours and dollars of litigation. Rather than consider the cannibal should be placed elsewhere, like a strait jacket with a muzzle in a padded cell, it was determined that his teachers must all be incompetent and seriously in need more training. We were also ordered to take advanced nonviolent physical restraint training. Mr. Arrow, Ms. Christian, and I quietly whispered amongst ourselves, "Why hadn't we been given this training to start..."

His classmates saw him as somewhat of a curiosity and avoided Hannibal Lecter at all cost. Mr. Arrow and I reasoned that if we could keep Hannibal Lecter happy, we could protect ourselves, our students, and all human beings within his biting range. Most days Mr. Arrow and Ms. Christian closely monitored Hannibal Lecter, while I supervised the rest of the class. Both of us creatively graded his papers, which was a challenge because 100% of the time his papers were off-topic and scary.

7 IRONMAN

In the mid-1980s there was a school district in Florida that only paid its teachers during the school year, meaning it was impossible to have the checks spread out over the summer. In those days there was no such thing as direct deposits so the last day of school we would all pick up our checks and run to the bank then worry about what how we would manage our money to cover all of our bills during the dry spell of summer.

It was a struggle for teachers to find full-time employment during the two months of off time, but I managed to get a job doing landscape work at commercial properties during the summer when the Florida sun is at its hottest and grass and other weeds grow at their fastest. For reasons that should be obvious, I chose not to mention that I was a teacher and never indicated that I had any sort of college degree, instead choosing to speak very little and just do my work.

Our clothes literally disintegrated from the sweat and exposure to flying material. On the landscape crew my task was usually to handle the mowers, which I believed was the most fun of the jobs. Another guy would be the edger so he would be catching an assortment of objects like pavement chips flying up into the face and other parts of the body. Still another guy had the worst job of all because he had the weed whacking chore. The shell-of-a-man who handled this task everyday was known as "Ironman".

On rare occasions we would take lunch together and find someplace with a little bit of shade where we could eat and replenish ourselves with water. Wilfredo would show up sporadically, as all of us did except Ironman who was always on the job, and whenever Wilfredo did show up, he was usually the group leader, due to his countless years on the trail. Although there was too much work, I think our boss tried to work us sporadically in the summer in order that we would not get too worn-out from never taking a break so he would not have to try to search for new employees who might steal or commit some sort of crime on his watch. "Better a devil that you know what they will do than one you don't yet know". We worked from before dawn until after dark on those long summer days. On one lunch Wilfredo asked Ironman where he got the jacked up tattoo on his arm and Ironman recounted the following story.

Ironman was in high school and he knew he was never going to make it to college, nor do I think he really wanted to go to college. Ironman learned that the Army would give him a bonus if he joined the artillery and an additional bonus was given for the task of loading nuclear shells in Germany. Army pay for enlisted men was far from great so he jumped at the bonus opportunity. Ironman remarked the dogs were always checking his unit for drugs and the stress of the job was tremendous. I don't know if he ever got into any drugs but assume he and his cohorts did, but I was certain that he did a hell of a lot of drinking.

Ironman said there would be drills in which young lieutenants would put a loaded and cocked 45 caliber pistol to his head as he carried a heavy nuclear round to the breach of his weapon. The nervous officer was almost always shaking and it drove Ironman crazy to think that just a little slip or an itch would end his life in faster than a second. I had always thought the USA would gradually escalate if things got crazy with the Soviets, but Ironman mentioned that the strategy was always to fire our full load immediately and God would sort it out. Ironman said he and his unit frequently got drunk as soon as they were off duty and one day they had all decided to go get a tattoo for no particular reason other than everybody in their group would have the same tattoo. Apparently they were all so drunk they couldn't even set up in the tattoo parlor stool hence the barely legible tattoo art on his arm.

On Fridays our boss would arrive and pay us off in cash. Typically babies' mothers, girlfriends, etc. would periodically appear on Friday afternoons and sit like vultures waiting for our boss to arrive or until they got too bored. When our boss arrived he gave the money directly to us and that's when the fun began. Wilfredo apparently had fathered plenty of children and this was his sole income, so there wasn't enough money to go around and it was like watching a female grudge-match battle-royale. There are television shows, movies, and countless music videos but none of them can approximate the ferocity and pitilessness of these ferocious females. Usually we would try to duck and cover to get out of the way while trying to make sure that we did not catch any of their glances out of mortal fear of becoming entwined in the melees. Occasionally one of these crazed females holding screaming babies or small children would attempt to finance money from us using the pretext that we worked with Wilfredo so we were equally responsible for the money that he owed them. We made ourselves very scarce on payday.

Ironman was married and his wife would appear on Friday out of nowhere begging for money to pay the rent. Since we usually got paid at the closest gas station, Ironman would quickly run and get beer before his desperate housewife would appear. Black Label Light was a $1.99 for a six pack, so that was his beer of choice and his salary for the week was about $300 in cash so you can do the math. Ironman drank so much that he was no longer permitted to drive a motor vehicle in the state of Florida. He would ride a bicycle to work and on Fridays he would attempt to drink as much as possible then ride his bike to wherever his latest apartment was located before his wife could catch-up with him. Ironman would even sling some beers around his waist and hips as he drove the bike so he could down a few brews while riding the bike. Ironman got picked up for driving under the influence while riding a bike, but what could the police do? There was no longer a Florida driver's license to be had for him and anybody can ride a bike without a license. The arrest for public intoxication would keep him in jail for a while but eventually he would be back on the street. Somehow or someway, Ironman's bike got destroyed and he didn't have enough money or the ability to get another one so he just walked the very crooked path to wherever he was currently staying due to being evicted from apartments for non-payment of rent.

When Ironman didn't come to work Middle School Mike took his place. Middle School Mike earned his name because one day when we were eating lunch Wilfredo confessed that he had to drop out of high school due to having babies. We did not doubt him for a minute based on the activities that we saw every Friday. Middle School Mike told us that he dropped out in the eighth grade, which even for our crew was pretty extreme. Middle School Mike was probably old enough to be in high school yet because he was a dropout, he could not get a driver's license due to not having the state required Verification Of Enrollment (VOE) and couldn't find anybody else that would employ him. Middle School Mike complained the worst thing about dropping out was missing out on the parties. When he was in school he was in contact with all the party kids and knew where to go but after he dropped out, they just didn't contact him and he admitted he became sort of a pest for them. Whenever he saw some of his former classmates they really had nothing in common and Middle School Mike just couldn't relate to what was going on with the teachers, assignments, social life, etc. of high school so they just avoided him like the plague.

In the fall at one of the high school football games that I was announcing, I took a break during halftime to go to the concession stand and met Middle School Mike by surprise.

30

He was trolling the stadium and was as surprised to see me at the game as I was to see him. He asked me what I was doing there and I said just going to see the game and talk about it. He asked me if I knew where there were any parties and I gave him the honest answer that I just didn't know. Middle School Mike was accustomed to this response. Middle School Mike said my voice sounded kind of like the announcer and laughed. Middle School Mike didn't linger too long because he needed to continue to try to find someone who would remember him and tell him where the parties might be...

8 IVAN THE TERRIBLE

In a very large urban school district there are going to be children from foreign backgrounds, because whenever there is a disaster somewhere on the planet, we always manage to get the refugees. Africans fleeing Ebola, Syrians fleeing ISIS, etc. Ivan the Terrible came from the former Soviet Republic of Kazakhstan. There really wasn't any fighting in his home country, but Ivan the Terrible expressed the concept that because he was a true Russian in a Central Asian republic that he faced discrimination. Ivan the Terrible didn't come with any paperwork, which was expected, but his English was surprisingly good considering that he had only spent a few weeks in the district's magnet school for recent immigrants before being released to the regular population in what was termed the least restrictive environment.

Ivan was a tiny kid but seemed to be very worldly. Perhaps a little too bright for his supposed age of 14... As mentioned previously, we didn't have any paperwork so the school district just kind of guessed his age and took his word to be the truth. Ivan the Terrible was placed in my low level World Geography class. He was just a little too smart, but again since he was a new student he was judged to be not capable of the advanced placement or other upper level classes until his English improved.

No information ever arrived about Ivan the Terrible.
Did he have parents in the United States?
He did not say.
Where was he living?
He did not say.
How did he get to the United States?
He did not say.
Ivan the Terrible did tell me that he had to flee Kazakhstan due to anti-Russian prejudice, but he didn't reveal much else.

In those days, each classroom had a set of four computers for students to use and a teacher computer. We didn't have the technology to monitor the student computers other than a watchful eye. My students would enjoy playing a simulation, for which the district bought the rights, called "Sim City". This was a fantastic game for students to play because they learned about city planning. Every once in a while one of the students would cause a flood, earthquake, or alien attack to see how their city could react. I allowed the natural disasters and occasionally would let them do the UFO's, but by and large, wanted the kids to stick to urban planning. Music videos, gaming, social media, and porn were the common distractions from the computer assignments which got the students in trouble.

Ivan the Terrible was observed watching a movie that had not yet been released in theaters. Ivan told me that he could get me any movie I wanted because he had done this for a living in Kazakhstan. He joyfully boasted that our computers were not state-of-the-art and that he would even fix both my school and home computer to work a lot faster and better, by removing a lot of the garbage that was installed on the American computers. I respectfully declined and mentioned that obtaining films and selling them before they had been released in the movie theaters was considered illegal in the USA. Ivan the Terrible probably knew this but he gave me an incredulous look, followed by a smile and a wink.

A few days later we were working on the computers and Ivan and again recommended he could fix my school computer so would be better, or at least as a teacher I should contact the internet technology guys to have them fix my machine. Within the blink of an eye a message appeared on the screen saying there was a bomb that was going to destroy my computer, followed by a message from Ivan that he was laughing. I looked back and Ivan boasted that he did it but was not even near the student computers.

About a week or two later some gentlemen, who were a little too sophisticated, came to my door and escorted me to the conference room where they asked pointed questions about computer use in my classroom. The questions were worded in such a way so as not to tip me off to anything. I gave honest answers and was actually oblivious to what or who they were really looking for. Apparently the same bomb message that appeared on my computer appeared on every computer in the district. Ivan the Terrible never returned to my classroom, nor did anyone ask for his grades. Ivan the Terrible just vanished.

9 JACK AND DIANE

This is a little ditty about Jack and Diane, two American kids growing up in the Florida Promised Land. Diane showed up to my classroom without any paperwork and told me that she had just transferred in from somewhere else and the counselor would get her paperwork so she could be added to my roster.

This did not raise an eyebrow, because so many kids were leaving the Rust Belt with parents hoping to strike it rich in Florida that we just couldn't keep track of the deluge. I knew her paperwork and documents would arrive eventually, so I gave her a syllabus and halfheartedly asked for her information because I knew she probably didn't know her new address, new phone number, etc. I asked her what she had been studying in US History and she said she couldn't remember. Often times these children arrived either with one parent or no parent due to unpleasant home circumstances, so they often were experiencing recent traumatic stress, which made getting any kind of answers problematic.

Diane's attendance was sporadic and her appearance was disheveled, but hardly unusual, and fairly typical. It was clear her heart and mind were on other things because she just looked out the window, like many students, and daydreamed.

Jack arrived a week or two later and fed me the same kind of story about his schedule being changed and paperwork coming sometime later. Jack was also somewhat out of it, which was typical of most of the 11th graders that I received. Jack's attendance was sporadic, too.
We used to have an area for teachers to meet in what had once been a textbook storage area, but due to rapid growth it had been converted to an place for teachers to eat because the teachers dining area was converted to a classroom. Due to my lunch schedule I would teach, lock the classroom, eat lunch, then go back to unlock the classroom and teach the same kids in the same classroom. This was referred to as a"split lunch" and was a direct result of serious overcrowding.

I used to eat lunch at a desk with Mr. William T Sherman, who wore a Union Army belt buckle every day and a bow tie. No one really knew his name; they just mentioned him as "that teacher that always wears a bow tie."

Mr. William T Sherman enjoyed every opportunity to relate to anyone who would listen about how much better things were up North and how much smarter the people were up North. I was tempted, but knew better than to ask him what he and all the people from up North were doing coming to Florida if up North things were so much better...

One afternoon during lunch Mr. William T Sherman got a shocked look on his face and remembered that he had forgotten to lock his classroom door. Since Mr. William T Sherman was a science teacher there were potentially chemicals and gas burners in the classroom that could be used for mischief, he swiftly left for his room in the middle of lunch. The administration warned us repeatedly about kids who supposedly would walk through the school and just check to see if doors were open in order to steal or cause trouble.

As Mr. William T Sherman entered his unlocked classroom, he discovered Jack and Diane, in the act of procreation on top of the lab table. Apparently their sporadic attendance was due to frequent indiscretions at school in unlocked rooms. The counselor came to me and told me they never should have even been in the same classroom with the same lunch because their parents had forbidden them to be anywhere near each other. For their "actions" they were suspended from school for 10 days.

After school I used to lift weights at the school's the weight room, but teachers were eventually forbidden from the over-crowded room because it was needed by students so I began to work out at a gym located not too far from campus. The local police force frequented the gym and I became friends with one of the county sheriffs. The sheriff related to me that his wife had given him a very bad time and accused him of cheating on her. I was in a little bit of a state of shock, because he went to my church and the other cops had never indicated, even jokingly, that he was anything less than a hard-core Christian who although he worked vice would never even consider an extramarital affair and there were plenty of opportunities for indiscretions in their line of work. I asked him how his wife could come to such a crazy conclusion.

Well, the sheriff related that his wife returned from her work before his arrival and found lipstick stains on a glass for which he denied but had no explanation. A heated argument ensued. The sheriff seemed to think someone, probably a female, came into their house without forced entry then drank something and departed without stealing anything. Who would do such a thing and why?

Life was pretty strained for the sheriff and his wife until the following day their neighbors had a huge argument about the same topic in which each believed the other spouse was cheating and just making excuses to cover their dirty deeds. Apparently someone got into the next door neighbor's home smoked their cigarettes, drank their beers, and even sampled some of the more expensive makeup. The messed up bedsheets, alcohol, and cigarettes in the nearby homes exploded the tranquil neighborhood into an extreme zone of marital strife as accusations, innuendo, and gossip took their toll.

Sensing this was no longer random, the wily sheriff set a trap. The sheriff recognized that this was a case of breaking and entering, but what was the motive? He was more than a little surprised that no theft was involved, so he convinced one of his neighbors leave the back door unlocked while he had an undercover comrade from the county sheriff's department stake out the house. Sure enough it was our suspended students Jack and Diane trying to make-out in any location they can.

Jack and Diane related when they first started going into people's homes they were careful, but as their pattern continued they became more and more flippant and sloppy. Jack and Diane even took delight in their critical ratings to the police about the various items in the homes that they enjoyed, because the indulged in everything at every home so the only concoction they did not partake was *"Abstinence at the Geyser"*...

There was absolutely no remorse from Jack and Diane, and they confessed they held a smug sense they had proudly livened up their quiet suburban area by their antics.

In the subdivision there was some tension relief after their arrest, although some suspicious spouses probably never completely trusted each other again.

10 JAKE THE WILD BOY FROM JAMAICA

Early in my career we received our paychecks once a month and ran as fast as we could to the nearest bank to deposit the money, because there was no such thing as direct deposit and the banks had long lines. Most of us wrote our checks in advance and paid our bills by mail that day or the day before so the bills would be paid in time. Try to picture the teacher parking lot as the start of the Kentucky Derby with teachers racing from the parking lot to their banks and not a moment to spare. Of course on the horse track the jockeys are always aware of their competition so we were all keenly aware of who went where. On the routes to the various banks in the community where the herds of teachers would pull off, there were shacks with metal bars on the windows and catchy signs in various languages stating that in these places you could get the best deal in sending money to foreign countries. One of our janitors made that her first stop on every paycheck.

We all knew she was sending money to Jamaica to keep her son alive and doing well. Occasionally she would complain about how her family kept asking for more cash to take care of her son's educational expenses, food, medicine, etc. Her husband left her and she didn't have much opportunity to make any money in Jamaica, so she moved to Florida to work as a janitor. Needless to say, her income was not much. She wore the same clothes every day. The coaches felt very sorry for her because she had to clean up the locker rooms during summer practice sessions when the smell, heat, humidity, and bugs made cleaning the locker rooms a living hell. We would give her T-shirts and she would wear them until they disintegrated because all of her money was going to take care of her son and like a good mother she always put her son first.

One day before school started, I was on an errand from the coaching staff and saw her in the open hallway. The Janitor was overjoyed and told me that over the years she had eventually saved up enough money to go to Jamaica to bring her son back so he could live with her. She also lamented that all of the increasingly greater amounts of money she unwittingly sent to Jamaica had been spent on drugs so she found her son in the jungle living like a wild animal. She knew that I would have her son in class so she sacredly charged me to make sure that he finally got a good education.

Jake's skin was crusty, probably from not taking baths. Jake's gums and teeth were bloody with rotted food from never brushing/flossing his teeth. Jake did not know how to use a restroom so we had some of the football players and I take him into the restroom and he was terrified and ran screaming when he saw toilet flush and the blow-dryer. Instead Jake would just go to relieve himself at any time and any place he wanted. Jake also felt like he was in a carnival because he had never seen a school so it was like going from one carnival ride to the next with no rhyme or reason. We had to have football players escort him to his classes. Keep in mind in those days we didn't have cops or cell phones on the campus so teachers and administrators had a lot of leeway to do what was best for the child. So long as no other student contacted the police, television, or their parents everything stayed cool…

The rodent and bug population at the school disappeared because Jake was faster than both and loved to eat them. The students really enjoyed seeing him do his thing with the insects but were thoroughly creeped out when he ate the rodents. They also liked the fact that he could copy the sound of any animal, so they would tease Jake in order to get him to react. It was tough to get the kids to stop, but frankly fun to listen to Jake perfectly mimic the exact sounds of all the critters.

Since Jake was one of my students, and his kind mother had requested that I make every effort to give him a good education, I tried to communicate with Jake but hit a stonewall, so I contacted my friend that was a reading teacher and asked her to try to help. She also knew the janitor and was more than willing to do whatever she could to help. Unfortunately she also hit the proverbial stonewall, so we were both able, given enough time and paperwork, to get someone from the district to test Jake. The district expert gave Jake a test to see what languages he understood, but the answer came back "negative", because Jake did not speak any language, although some English was detected.

Jake's days were numbered. Jake grew up in the jungle so whenever he got the urge he would go after the females just like he had seen animals do it in the jungle. This led to big problems. At first I had the members of the football team form a Berlin Wall around Jake during his escorts to class and while in class.

The dress code was always impossible to enforce during the warm weather in Florida, but Jake was able to make every girl in the school go far beyond the bare minimum of the dress code because when he got the urge no female was safe from provoking his attentions-especially if they had any skin showing. Why was every girl at the high school wearing bulky sweat pants in 100+ F temperatures? The answer is Jake the Wild Boy from Jamaica…

Do you remember when you read the statement "So long as no other student contacted the police, television, or their parents everything stayed cool…"? Well, with all the girls in heavy sweatpants things were definitely not cool, so Jake was quickly and quietly sent to another school.

11 JOHNNY CAN'T READ

Johnny's arms were huge and he was a very talented freshman football player. He been found in the Okefenokee Swamp of Georgia and brought to our school. Johnny and all of his family worked at the airport handling baggage, which probably gave him the monster sized arms and strength. Johnny's older brother was a senior and star on the football team who could play almost any position both offense or defense due to his great strength and physical ability, so it was believed that Johnny would do the same and maybe even better.

Johnny was placed in my class and always was very polite and well mannered. Johnny could be a clown, but was always good-natured, even though he was learning his boundaries. The goal of every teacher is not just to see that their kids pass, but also to instill a desire for learning. I noticed that Johnny occasionally misspelled his name and at first thought it might be because his body might be bruised from football. Occasionally, when asked to read, he would make mistakes and say words that were not on the page.

Could Johnny have had dyslexia? Maybe even some scoptic issues? Concussion? One of my coach friends did a field test for concussion and Johnny passed. I expressed my concerns to his mother and requested a visual specialist to see Johnny. The specialist was extremely impressed with Johnny's high intelligence, but could not find any evidence of visual impairment. Still Johnny couldn't read.

One day I was at the steamboat house restaurant with some of the teachers from school. I left to go use the men's room and saw Johnny perplexed standing by the bathroom doors. In place of a symbol, the men's room was called the Robert E Lee room and the ladies bathroom was called the Annabel Lee room. Both had steamboats as symbols next to the names. I spoke to Johnny for a moment or two before going to the restroom and asked him what he was doing there. He seemed a little embarrassed, and just told me "Oh, he was there with his family getting a good meal and asked about the food". When I asked him why he was standing next to the two doors, he kind of looked dumbfounded at me and at that point I knew the reason but did not have sufficient proof.

Back at school I asked Johnny to spell "Orlando" on a piece of paper and he wrote "MCO" which is the code for McCoy field, the Orlando international airport. Just to be sure, I asked Johnny to spell "Miami" and he wrote "MIA". Okay, probably we can think of more accurate tests, but the conclusion was clear. Johnny had learned the symbols and went through life discovering and decoding words based on previous knowledge. He was extremely bright, but just had not learned to read and was ashamed of his condition. I made sure that Johnny got some reading help, but tried to hide the fact from him that he was being taught the alphabet and how to read. It was hard to play the game of maintaining his self-esteem, and building him up, while teaching very basic concepts so he was kept away from the other students with various excuses.

The specialist who tested Johnny came to the same conclusion. Johnny was amazing at using coping strategies due to his high level of intelligence and was able to trick many people into believing that he could read. The specialist spent unbelievable amounts of time working with Johnny and was one of those kinds of people who go above and beyond her job for the good of everyone with whom she interacts. This specialist really wasn't even supposed to help teach people to read, because she had a full load just testing students so everything she did for Johnny was done on the sly. I think she really liked teaching reading, but there was no certificate, reward, honor, or cash payment; just knowing that she had put untold extra hours to help a student was enough.

12 JUMPING JACK FLASH

Students gathered on the second floor parapet very rapidly and all of the sudden the typical noise between classes dissipated. Within seconds a student jumped from the second floor to the first floor and took off running. Initially, there were some loud yells, but the great mass of humanity modeled on to their classes talking about the jumper and hypothesizing what he might do next.

When the students arrived in my classroom I asked them what happened and was met with a stone wall of silence that I knew I just couldn't crack so I gave up.

A week or so later I was in the second-floor hallway and saw the students begin to congregate. Money was being waved around and I saw, out of the corner of my eye, a boy with a large brownish-orange Afro jump to the first floor. With cat-like reflexes he swiftly tumbled in a manner similar to someone who had been trained with how to fall in a judo class, or how to land from the Army parachute without getting hurt and take evasive action to disappear from enemy patrols. The students felt it was their duty to protect him so they purposely blocked my vision and the vision of other teachers until he got away.

A faculty meeting was called and an all-points-bulletin issued on Mr. Jumping Jack Flash. We were told to try to identify him and contact a counselor, as well as the deans, because it was rumored that he was doing this for cash and bets had been placed. In those days we didn't have television cameras, and the students were not about to tell us anything relating to Mr. Jumping Jack Flash. We reasoned that he would try to continually surpass his jumping exploits until eventually he got hurt. The staff was instructed to attempt to walk the second-floor as frequently as possible and stay outside of the classrooms in order to monitor students.

One day I saw a slim boy with the same peculiar hair color. He looked as if he might be a mix between African-American and white, but the red eyes gave him away as an African-American albino. He was wearing a green jumpsuit and very light tennis shoes which seemed to me to be telltale signs that he was Mr. Jumping Jack Flash who jumped for cash, cash, cash.

I knew better than to mention jumping, which would make him skittish, so I discussed my role as assistant track coach and tried to make small talk. I lamented that we had some amazingly fast runners, good hurdlers, but we really needed someone doing pole-vault. In fact, we actually could use someone just like him. But then again, he would have to enjoy jumping and doing aerobatics and then falling into cushions for the applause of the people watching the track meet and potential awards. I asked him how his grades were, then explained Florida's "no pass, no play" rule, as a very open ended yet nonchalant attempt to get him to join. I told him we could put him pretty much anywhere on the team because we were desperate for athletes and tutoring could be arranged if he might need it. Running at top speed in the Florida heat is not an endeavor that most students or even adults find comfortable, so there would always be openings. As an added enticement, I mentioned the not so obvious fact that since so few students were cut out for track, scholarships were not too difficult to obtain.

Mr. Jumping Jack Flash was never apprehended, but a new athlete joined the track team as a pole-vaulter and I'm sure the deans were happy not to have to deal with another discipline issue.

13 MAGIC MIKE

Magic Mike was 21 years old and still in a ninth grade World Geography class because he was classified as Special Ed due to an extreme lack of short-term memory, probably amplified by ADHD. The World Geography class was required for graduation, so he had to pass it even though he could not retain the material, which is probably why he had been unsuccessful in the class since he was 14 or 15 years old. Magic Mike was assigned Mr. Arrow as his in class support teacher. Magic Mike's memory was so bad he was directed to his classes by Mr. Arrow who also worked hard to help Magic Mike remember anything and to keep Magic Mike awake.

Magic Mike awake? Why was he so sleepy? Well Magic Mike liked to dance all night, hence he was always sleepy, couldn't pay attention, and rarely attended school, which just might explain why he was a 21-year-old but couldn't pass a low-level ninth-grade class.

In case anybody hasn't gotten be in the initial alliteration from the title, Magic Mike was a professional dancer at a club where he would dance, dance, dance while hosts of women put money in his pants, pants, pants. Whoops, he wasn't wearing any pants for most of the show, so in his G string the multitudes of women their money would throw...

When he was in school Magic Mike wore designer outfits and styles with brand names I could never recognize. One day walking through some boutiques, I noticed some of these items worn by Magic Mike and my jaw dropped to the floor when I realized the prices being paid for such items. Perhaps these duds were job-related perks?

One time while Magic Mike meandered down the hallway barely awake with Mr. Arrow and I at his side, a moderately young female teacher spied at him, got a sullen, somewhat scared look on her face, and moved very quickly in another direction, which only confirmed how popular/memorable he must have been. Of course the young girls in the class were enamored with him, too. Magic Mike frustrated their young hearts because he would forget their names, words, and actions instantly.

Mr. Arrow came to the conclusion the best way to help Magic Mike retain geographic information would be to put it together in rhythms for him to repeat incessantly almost like, you guessed it, dance routines. It worked!

14 PINBALL WIZARD

The Pinball Wizard never listened, never spoke and couldn't see anything, but he wasn't a deaf, dumb and blind kid. Instead, he was up all night, inhaling monster drinks and playing video games, so when he came into the classroom he was near comatose. His hands always at the ready, and his eyes were set deeply in the sockets of his head waiting for some sort of stimulus that was never coming. He looked like he was either going to bite the dust or pull the trigger any second. I used to think to myself, "This 14-year-old boy is a heart attack waiting to prematurely happen."

The Pinball Wizard had disciples following him around, waiting for him to utter some cryptic words of knowledge that would forever enhance their gaming abilities. Yes, he was treated like an Olympic athlete in our presence due to his superior gaming skills. I was told that he had a following on YouTube, similar to a mega-popstar for his ability to decipher games and his skill with his wrists on a mouse, keyboard, or joystick. He was the ultimate young gun of the gaming world and he was in my class.

Ultimately, however, he did absolutely not a single assignment in any class. When given a test he seemed to be in some hypnotic state, so we couldn't even get him to put his name on his paper. The thousand yard stare never seem to change.

His behavior was the same in every class and we eventually were able to have his mother come to school for a conference. Keep in mind each one of us called the parent and left messages multiple times so it seemed the best to eventually have a meeting with all the teachers to discuss similar behaviors. The parent immediately lashed out at the teachers for not knowing how to teach and not reaching her son's needs. I wanted to say that if it was just one teacher she might be right, but if seven diverse teachers and the counselor all had the same issues then maybe, perhaps, it could be her son and we were only meeting to try to find a successful method to reach her beloved boy.

The logical parental solution was to have her son do the work, then play the video games, and have a reasonable bedtime hour. One of the teachers even suggested taking the cords from the computer, so the Pinball Wizard could not wake up at night and start playing while the mother was asleep. The father was permanently off the keyboard in his life.

In a school where we were told by our principal "our duty is to graduate the students not teach them life lessons", the Pinball Wizard still managed to fail because there was nothing we could do for someone who made absolutely no effort.

About seven or eight years later the student made posts online about wanting to shoot up the school and kill anything that moved for ruining his life. He was arrested and the school did some active shooter lockdown drills without telling any of the new students exactly why. The students felt they were being picked on for no reason and grew irritated.

Of course, with a plethora of new games and gaming gurus, none of the current students knew him so his long past god-like status was about as far removed from our school as the planet beyond Pluto. There were barely any teachers the remembered the Pinball Wizard, but I remembered him. When I saw his very scary mug shot on the news I couldn't help but think that I once had a Major-League-Gamer, of world-renown fame in first-person shooter gameplay, who super-succeeded in getting electronic badges of absolutely no earthly value, and captivated a multitude of face-less internet fans who followed his every twitch, yet how did he finish. "Game Over"

15 THE GIRL WITH NO PANTS

The girl with no pants rarely attended class. Mention was made to the associate principal and to her counselor, but the common reply was to contact the parent before any action could be taken by the administration.

After attempting various telephone numbers in the system which all proved to be fictitious, I eventually encountered the number which worked. The mother was of very limited English, there was absolutely no possibility of getting a translator, and I was fearful that anything I might say could become misinterpreted resulting in me ending up in handcuffs on the television as some kind of a nasty perverted teacher, so I chose to try to only mention to the mother only that her daughter was missing class, which the mother did not seem to believe. I knew no progress was going to be made and imagined that the girl told her mother a bunch of different stories in their native language of Tagalog which the mother believed more than some English-speaking teacher the mother could barely comprehend.

Understanding the girl rarely attended, and when she did attend class she was constantly on her phone, I tried to do the best with what I had. Makeup work and offers a tutorial were given, but any make up work received from her was copied from someone else and she never attended tutorials. What to do?

Well, the real problem wasn't even her grades or lack of attendance, but the fact that she attended class only wearing a shirt...

Both the boys and the girls couldn't help but pass glances at her. The boys' minds focused directly to her. The girls were openly hostile with their glances, whispers, and what must've been harsh tweets/texts/snap chats. The disheveled look on her face and football jersey, sleep shirt, or men's button-down seemed to indicate she was doing something else other than strenuously going to class, but I dared not acknowledge the obvious. This girl had come from advanced placement to my low level class, so apparently I was not the only cognizant instructor who was keeping quiet about the elephant in the room, or should I say the girl with no pants in the room...

16 THE SAINT

I was working at the only high school in a small district were discipline was fairly lackadaisical. Everybody knew everybody else, down to whose family was in the little community first in the 1830s. When kids would mess up, someone in the community would call the coach or a teacher so the students knew they were under watch both in class and out. I had an eye operation which ended my coaching career, so my job was to work the detention hall (D-Hall) after school every day and on Saturdays.

The Saturday D Hall meant that I would arrive at the school before sunrise at around six o'clock in the morning, unlock the front door of the school, go through the halls turning on the lights and eventually get to my classroom and unlock it. I was the only one on campus and they originally told me to hold the D Hall in the auditorium, but there was no phone in the auditorium so if there was ever any trouble I would be out of luck, therefore I went to my classroom. In my classroom I would watch the kids and also hopefully, on rare occasions, be able to get something done.

The aforementioned pattern would continue every year and I was paid about a dollar more than minimum wage but was anxious to get it. For many years my salary was actually lowered rather than increased, perhaps because they knew I needed the money and would work hard. The administration treated me pretty well so I had no complaints.

The students would arrive at seven o'clock and would stay with me for either three hours or five hours. The students would take a break after 1 1/2 hours so students could be given the opportunity to use a restroom and stretch. I would stand outside the bathroom while the students went in and did their business. At the three-hour mark most of the students would leave. About an hour later we would take another restroom break, then at 12 o'clock after five hours had past, the last of the students would be released. It was difficult to get a three-hour D Hall, but the five hour D Hall was an absolutely rare event. A student in our small town would have to do something horrific to earn a five hour D Hall.

Sometimes before seven o'clock, I would chat with the students about what they did and try to counsel them. Most freely told me what they did, and expressed some regret. Every once in a while there would be a real hard case who would blame other people for his or her actions. The vast majority of students who earned detention hall on Saturday only visited detention hall one time in their lives, so The Saint was a very unusual case because he was a frequent flyer.

During the whole time in detention the students had to do school work or they could read school-related material which I would provide for them. If a student showed up with nothing school related they were to be sent home, but since some students finished their school work early I made sure they had something to do. I paid the students from the wood shop class to make a magazine rack for me to hold extra books and magazines. Usually this meant National Geographic or some sort of scholastic material.

The Saint caught my attention because he was assigned the hall on Saturday for five hours more than once and more than once I had to throw him out of the Saturday D Hall. What did he do in the D- hall which might cause him to be forced to leave? Well, one time he decided to show porn and another time he brought the marijuana magazine "High Times" which she showed off to the other students, while ranting about the merits of smoking the Devil's lettuce amid the silence of the D-hall.

The Saint's father was a single parent, probably in his 40's who drove brand-new jet black Porsche 944. Every Saturday morning the car would land into the parking lot, drop off The Saint, and launch into the oblivion.

The father was a subdivision developer with boatloads of cash. The father even had a street in one of his developments named after himself. He was well known to drive at ridiculously high speeds and whenever he was stopped he would get the ticket and then just pay the fee as if it was just a trifling matter to him. Eventually his insurance premiums rose higher than the Taipei Tower, but he really didn't care because he had so much money. The video game *Grand Theft Auto* had nothing on him and the movie series *Fast and the Furious* probably couldn't even approach his style of driving with the best of stunt drivers or computer graphics. Some police officers in town alluded to finding excuses for not daring to pursue after his car literally out of fear for their lives.

In addition to his car, The Saint's father spent a lot of his time with the knock-out single mother of one of my students. This flawlessly beautiful mother was absolutely beyond gorgeous and always wore the height of fashion. The vivacious mother had curves in all the right places, beautiful big eyes, perfect make-up, so she was in the sights of the wealthy single father as his next trophy wife. Eventually the two single parents married, but at this time they were just dating and The Saint was the proverbial squeaky third wheel. The single mother had an attractive daughter who was my student. The daughter was a nice girl and very popular. One day she revealed that her mother was dating The Saint's dad and how hard it was for her to play nice with The Saint. The girl wanted a letter jacket but really was not going to be a hardcore athlete or cheerleader, because she had to go with her mother to beauty parlors, tanning beds, and the gym, so she worked a deal with the librarian to do duty in the library to earn a letter jacket as part of a "Friends of the Library" varsity team. Not surprisingly many young males flocked to the library and took a keen interest in Library Science as a direct result of her stacking books. There was also a "Four Year Bus Rider" letter jacket, but this daughter drove a stylish new car, as did her mother, supplied by The Saint's dad so the bus rider jacket was out of the question.

It didn't take long to figure out that The Saint enjoyed negative attention. In fact he craved negative attention with an insatiable desire. Perhaps he wanted attention from his father, but the father cared less and less for the son and more and more for his smoking hot girlfriend. The father even cared so little for the antics that he began to send associates to deal with his son and the school's administration. The Saint's bad behavior tactics did not even have a forlorn flicker of hope to gather his father's attention. To be honest I did not think The Saint's antics were an effort to get his father's attention, rather just the pure thrill of outrageous misbehavior, similar to what his father modeled in driving so recklessly. Could we say, like father like son?

One day I happened to be called in with a female associate principal, The Saint, and his father's girlfriend for a meeting about the latest antics of The Saint., when the girlfriend's phone rang. In plain view the phone ID that said "Jackhammer" was calling and on the girlfriend's phone the ID was "Happy Bang Bang". The female associate principal and I did our best to think of anything other than the obvious. I tried to divert the mental picture by concentrating on the Mojave Desert, the Atchafalaya Swamp, and even the Mongolian tundra in order to keep my mind off of the repercussions of the call signs, but it was hopeless. The female associate principal also tried to hide her imagination, but began to slightly blush. The telltale attempts at poker faces just didn't work. A strained silence ensued. The girlfriend caustically retorted "Yeah, I know what you're thinking and I own it".

Reckless? Outrageous? The Saint discovered that he thought it might be funny to spray the fire extinguisher in a crowded hallway into a multitude of students, thereby ruining their clothes, hair, makeup, etc. and causing a big commotion. The Saint was unbelievably lucky that Fire Chief Rick did not know what he had done, otherwise, The Saint would've probably been incarcerated for life or given the death penalty.

The Dean was a kindhearted man from Palestine Texas, who managed to save The Saint by getting a refill on the fire extinguisher in a sly way so that Fire Chief Rick could never figure it out. The kindhearted Dean responded to Fire Chief Rick's interrogation that he was taking the initiative to get a brand-new fire extinguisher refill before the refill date just to be extra sure that everything would be in tiptop shape for fire safety, hence the prior to obligatory expiration refill date for the fire extinguisher tag. Fire Chief Rick actually took this as a positive indicator of Fire Chief Rick's draconian fire safety agenda and gave a rare non-sarcastic smile to the kindhearted Dean from Palestine.

Before people were as sensitive to the LGBT community, The Saint decided to wear a miniskirt to class without panties. No one in the room was amused and his hysteria, which was really a chance for him to jump up and down and show everybody his undercarriage, caused him another five hours of Saturday D Hall.

Every year there was a male beauty pageant in which the guys from the school would get the latest tuxedos to model in a pageant before the homecoming game. The pageant was really a sales promotion for the local men's formal wear store and a lucrative fundraiser for charity, but nobody said anything. The boys would wear the tuxedos, answer some questions, and do a talent. Usually the questions were done in a tongue-in-cheek manner. For example, what is your favorite song would be answered with replies like "I'm a Barbie Girl", "I'm Not a Girl-Not Yet a Woman" etc. The boys would lift weights, toss a football, play musical instruments, dance, and so forth. The show was always a sellout and was a fun opportunity for some comedy, as well as a chance for the girls to see some of the cutest boys at school being silly. Somehow The Saint appeared and managed to unexpectedly strut on to the stage in high heels and a bikini and make extremely inappropriate comments. The Saint was never LGBT, he just liked to be hated for doing the wrong things.

Realizing The Saint's propensity for doing the wrong thing, I thought it best to try to get him on the right track. This may sound counterintuitive, but I offered to give him a free cup of coffee, with what-ever flavor or extras that he wanted if he could survive six Saturday D halls with me without doing something to get himself thrown out. Some of the other students were horrified that I would make this offer, but I was desperate because having to routinely deal with a sociopath every Saturday for five hours was beginning to get on my nerves. The time he took a dump in the hallway, was really the last straw, which led to the coffee idea. Surprisingly this worked. The Saint continued to cause trouble everywhere, except in Saturday D- hall so he relished his free cup of coffee as a frequent flyer promotion. (Regular coffee with cream and sugar, just in case you're curious) The Saint was offered a free doughnut of any flavor that he wanted with his coffee if he could behave for the next six weeks.

I fully expected to have to purchase the doughnuts and wondered what the next promotion would have to be for the most frequent inmate in the history of Saturday D Hall. Astonishingly I didn't see much or hear much of anymore exploits of The Saint. In the back of my mind I wondered, had he been sent to prison, withdrawn from school, been devoured by Fire Chief Rick, or gotten crossways with the government and sent to Guantánamo?

At the end of the school year, I had to race to get my students' grades done early because it was less than a half day of school and I was assigned to do the D Hall for the rest of the day in order for students to get makeup credit for hours that they had missed during the year. You'd be amazed at how many hours of school a teenager can miss and how many students needed to make-up hours in such a small community.

By this time the cafeteria was completely closed with all the vending machines absolutely empty, so there was nothing other than a water fountain. I talked to the kindhearted Dean from Palestine and asked for permission to order pizza for the students. Due to the fact that they would be stuck in the auditorium with me for many hours and there was no opportunity for anything. Hungry kids get Hangry and that's a place you don't want to be with 80 teenage eating machines for upwards of 5 hours.

Originally I bought pepperoni pizzas because one slice would be my lunch as well, but some of the Muslim students objected and their parents raised a fit, so I started ordering just cheese pizza at the end of the school year. It was less expensive but still a big chunk of money out of my pocket, and I was dealing with high medical bills, so the kindhearted Dean from Palestine agreed to help me with some of the cost.

I had to go to the other end to school to get the pizzas and managed to see The Saint about to leave campus with his belongings. I teased him about not showing up for Saturday D Hall or any detention hall, and lightheartedly toyed with him by asking if he wished to sit out in the auditorium for six or eight hours with me and I would let him get some pizza. The Saint laughed and said he had changed his ways. A girl came up and held his hand. Frankly I was surprised because The Saint had the reputation of being the devil himself, but this young girl, who was a devout Christian and member of the Campus Crusade for Christ, held his hands and they both described his amazing transformation from the dark side and their relationship with each other and Jesus. That was the last time I saw The Saint.

17 SONGSTER

I was hired as a science teacher in large metropolitan area in the Midwestern United States located along the Great Lakes. Decades before the urban school had been the domain of many future prominent leaders in the city, state, and nation. Business had been booming and the executives were making outrageous salaries, which led the employees to demand their fair share of the profits. Union demands increased. When the workers felt they did not get what they deserved, the workers routinely disrupted the production so quality control became an issue and prices for their products were easily beat by foreign competitors. People could no long afford the items and did not want products they would have to fix or repair daily so sales diminished. Taxes became quite high and services dwindled, prompting businesses to leave and unemployment to skyrocket. What had once been an upwardly mobile land of opportunity became a desolate wasteland. Voters elected leaders who promised more and more but always seemed to deliver less and less. People became resentful of their political leaders, as well as the business leaders, who all seemed to vanish before prosecution. There was a large, corrupt political machine in the city that had operated for probably 100 years or more and was not leaving. The party kept itself in power by making a scapegoat out of the rich corporations, business leaders, and opposing political party although the other party almost never won a seat, even as dog catcher.

My first day started before the school year began, when I was introduced to the science room, which had no equipment whatsoever. I asked the principal where the supplies would be, thinking the supplies must be in some sort of a storage closet but was told there were no supplies (nor textbooks), and if I was a good teacher I could teach the kids by creation of my own high yield strategies

Probably the biggest thing which caused me concern was rotten food and stains everywhere in the science room. The stink was real. I again went to the principal and mentioned the condition of the room, but she said the janitors were paid only to sweep and that I should concern myself with educating the kids while the janitorial staff took care of more pressing issues. Two out of every three light bulbs was non-functioning in the entire three-story school, so I made some flippant comment that yes, I understood based on the lack of lighting, but the principal fired back that as a money-saving policy the school had unplugged two out of every three light bulbs. Gosh, I knew I was in trouble with the principal before the school year even started, but really liked the paycheck and signing bonus, so I figured I would stay. Besides drinking the mystical Kool-Aid that she was brewing did not seem so bad.

Later that day I was venomously informed, a former NBA basketball player was re-hired and he could only teach science, so I would be assigned to be an English teacher. There would be another English teacher working with me, so again if I was a good teacher, I should be able to teach anything and should prepare myself for English grammar. And, Oh by the way, there were no books, nor materials because our district was so far advanced in the future of individual educational instruction that we would have the students use their own phones to look up materials in self-paced instruction.

The first day of school saw 45 students per classroom with only 30 desks. The air-conditioning was not working so even after Labor Day it was an inferno. I asked the students to open the windows and just sit on the window sills until the counselors would eventually balance classes. No student even spoke, so I did the manual labor myself. The principal showed up unexpectedly on that first day and said she was checking on every room then made a very nasty glance at me and told me to step outside. In the dimly lit hallway she got into my face and asked me what I thought I was doing, but I didn't have an answer because I did not understand her question. The principal said that by opening up the blinds and having the kids sit near the window the gangsters would exactly know who to target and a maelstrom of gunfire would be directed at the school. The principal was explicit in making sure that the blinds and the windows were always absolutely shut tight for that reason and if I didn't toe the line I would be literally smoked.

The other English teacher told me she had been in the district for a number of years and advised me to join the Union as fast as possible. She told me to keep my mouth shut and everything would be good. She matter-of-factly advised me that for any important discipline issue not to waste my time, but to document and keep a set of additional copies because there were no locks on the doors due to the students previously locking the door and gang raping a teacher. This English teacher had a classroom of 45 students as well, so she said she could not help me but she suggested I just better keep the kids amused. This lady brought in a television and DVD player and rented movies every day. So long as there was no news-worthy violence in the room, nobody cared and she said nonchalantly that she was such a frequent renter, that she began to get many of the movie rentals free. None of our computers worked and she cautioned me that anytime anyone streamed anything via computer it would leave a trail that could lead to termination which even the Union couldn't stop. The students also willfully used apps on their phones to take control of the computers and cause mayhem out of boredom.

How to keep the audience from being bored? The AP English teacher would have his students read recipes and make food in one of the science rooms. He was highly commended because the students liked learning how to cook, since most of their culinary experience was microwave or fast food. I was told this AP English teacher even got a special commendation from our principal for teaching the kids how to boil noodles in order to make spaghetti. Perhaps this was some of the food that I saw plastered to the walls and floor in the science room?

Our school had an 11% pass rate.

Generous bonuses were paid to high-performing schools. The principal really wanted to get a bonus. Her strategy was to have all of the teachers repeatedly go to training sessions to improve their ability to teach, which would result in higher standardized test scores and that all-important bonus. If the school continued to fail, the principal knew that she would get canned and some new favorite flavor-of-the-month, guru would replace her. She did not want to gamble on the chances of landing a cushy job at central office downtown, or try her hand as a consultant with bad scores so we were told to only give the following grades "A+, A, A-, B+, B, B- , C+, C, or C-" Any grade lower than a "C+" was an immediate visit to her office for "a counseling" after which she would change the grades herself. Students seemed to realize they could do anything and some were so brainwashed as to firmly believe life was going to be that easy. Integrity was a virtue missing from the school.

The other English teacher, Siskel and Ebert, really liked getting the days off to go to training and encouraged me to get as much training as possible to add to my resume plus it would be a day off from the kids and a chance to get some good food. It actually became kind of rare for the entire regular staff to be on campus on any one day, because most of the teachers were always in training.

I asked Siskel and Ebert about field trips for the students but she told me that the kids from the school were secretly banned by the bus driver's union because they had shown a propensity to try to cause bus accidents, so every time an off school activity was planned the bus drivers did "sick-outs" until no more requests were ever made...

We had some professional athletes show-up as part of their community service but the students heckled them mercilessly to the point some of the higher strung sports personalities almost erupted back and blew their probations. Still it was fun to see the stars and attempt to hear what wisdom they had to impart. Our science teacher was first in line to remind the pro athletes that he was once in the NBA and now he was a teacher, which really rocked their worlds.

Speaking of wisdom, the first chore was to teach the kids to spell, but that plan was countermanded by the principal because the state test did not check for spelling. I tried to explain that it was ludicrous to try to grade papers for a written test if even the expert code breakers at the NSA could not decipher what the student wrote…

Grading the papers was also an exercise in frustration because many of the students were completely illiterate. Siskel and Ebert never had the students write anything, but occasionally asked what movies they wanted to see and asked the AP English teacher to have his students see if they could make popcorn for her. Siskel and Ebert was flying under the radar and I was afraid I had already drawn enough flak to be constantly under the spotlight.

The students also really didn't care, because they had planned to follow the following pattern: They would party continually so they could both smoke and sell dope, get kicked out of their apartment, moved to a new apartment, and continue to get welfare. Since they were living in a cash economy, there was no reason for any job skill other than how to sling weed, kush, crack, bath salts, horse, etc.

The bathrooms in the school were largely nonfunctioning so students would urinate in the hallway or in the non-functioning water fountains. There was however, one student who actually used the bathroom, but as his local franchise. His name was "Songster".

Songster was quite the good dealer so he was constantly being pressured to make more cash by his superiors but he envisioned that his superiors would soon be dead, or incarcerated, and he would move up the chain of command. He constantly had to promote the quality, supply, and availability of the product he grinded so life was far from easy.

Songster would go into the restroom and start singing. He would sing in a very loud voice and always explained it was his constitutional right to sing because of freedom of religion and what was wrong with music since music is his happy place and love makes the world go around. Songster would belt out tunes like *"La Gasolina"* by Daddy Yankee, never knowing or caring that the song had nothing to do with gasoline and cars. Students would hear his voice and know exactly where to go to get filled up.

Songster sometimes sang for a long time, but usually it was just a short time. Although his voice was really not that great, over time it started to sound good. Songster was careful to leave out any curse words just in case there were any police nearby who might potentially make the huge mistake of trying to write a ticket for public profanity. Songster lamented "I just ain't got no time for that."

So long as no one messed with Songster or his business interests, nobody got hurt. Some new posses tried to take control of the jungle causing quite a bit of bloodshed. Rather than use a firearm, the typical method was to surround someone and chase after them to make them believe they were going beat them to death, but actually run them into traffic so they would be hit by a bus or vehicle and appear to be a suicide or consequences of slow jaywalking. That way nobody got any blame. The police just looked the other way, because they were not foolish enough to want to add to their paperwork or endanger their lives. The police were really interested in good community relations and keeping the media away, too. These were not the movie-style cops kicking-down doors to arrest bad guys, rather they were just trying to keep things calm in an area with a propensity for violence and crime. Occasionally rivals were stabbed in the throat with pencils, but no one said anything because "Snitches get Stiches."

Songster was my student so I asked him to write papers as if he was writing songs about make-believe events. Even though the struggle was real, his quick wit and imagination motivated him to do it, plus the Songster seemed to think that he had a real shot at perfecting his lyrical abilities and making it into the big-time world of music so he would achieve his dream of his own rap empire.

Songster also had a girlfriend known as The Fashionista, because every day. She wore a completely different outfit from head to toe. I asked the Fashionista how she could dress so well every day and she revealed that she would go to different stores purchased the latest fashion, never take off the tags, and return the clothing the next day so she always had an endless supply of free outfits. She even remarked that the salespeople were fully aware about her daily scheme, but liked it because her modeling was free advertising.

The Fashionista even acknowledged to me that before prom time she got every dress of every size of a similar design to hers, took them into the dressing room and then defecated and urinated on all of the other outfits except the one that fit her in order to be unique at prom because she feared copycats of her style. This time the salespeople at that store got angry with her and told her never to come back. Of course, they couldn't prove what she did, but they still knew it. In the city there are many shops so the results of her ruination of potential rival prom dresses at one store really didn't cramp her style.

The Fashionista was a target for other girls who were either jealous of her or interested in her boyfriend. The Fashionista recounted to me in tears that some of the girls had taken pictures of her which they quickly edited and sent to different television shows with her information as a potential case for the "*fashion police*" episodes. This kind of cruelty devastated the Fashionista, because in her dreams, she believed she was always the picture of beauty and extremely desirable in her fancy clothes, so when she got contacted by various television shows, it did not surprise her, but when she got wind that it was a cruel joke for the "*fashion police*" segment of the shows, it brought her self-esteem down more than a few notches.

One day my wife happened to be riding in her usual city bus, which got detoured from its usual route and wandered toward the school. A rival drug selling group decided to whack the Songster, so they got someone to pull the fire alarm and waited outside the school with knives and guns while have some other associates attempted to blow-up a gas station in another section to divert the attention and resources of the cops. Shots were conveniently fired from the grounds across from the school, so the principal never needed the report that there was any shooting on school grounds. The blades came out as rival gang members infiltrated the stunned crowd looking for Songster so they could slice him. The students knew what was going down because word traveled fast. Songster mysteriously wound up right next to the cops. When I got home to our apartment, my wife asked me how things went at school and I replied "Oh, Just the same old -same old. Another day in paradise".

My wife then lit into me with a pyroclastic eruption of verbal abuse about being a filthy liar by not telling her what she had seen when the bus made a detour around my school. I was caught unawares, because I had become hardened by the environment in which I worked. I explained to my wife that a teacher is a bit like a doctor. The teacher is trained to work with all kinds of students just like a doctor has all kinds of sick patients. The doctor diagnoses and prescribes medicine, in order to make sure that the patients get better. The teacher tries to instruct in order to make the students better. Neither the doctor nor the teacher get to pick their patients/students, but it's our job to make sure that we do our best with whoever walks through our door by any means necessary. My wife yelled at me, "Get out of that #%^& school by any *#%^ means necessary or there will be only one person living in this *#%^ apartment."

I comprehended my wife's directive completely and complied.

In the winter not too many years later when we were living in the distant suburbs, my bus happened to stop at a red light, and the windows of the bus began to shake from the base of a vehicle sound system that was so loud it felt like a minor earthquake. The noise and the beat were absolutely deafening, but what made this incident different from many others just like it, was the fact that I recognized the voice of Songster intermittently between the thunderous thuds of the beats. I think there were some vague references to his girlfriend known, amongst other descriptives, as the "Fashionista."

Was anything I did at that school for Songster partly the inspiration for the birth of a sensational Rap Star whose lyrics were so exceptionally brutal that most of his song was unplayable on public airwaves?

18 ZANY

Zany was amusingly unconventional and idiosyncratic. I was teaching Algebra II in the San Francisco Bay area when Zany was assigned to my classroom. As an ice-breaker I used to ask each student what he or she planned for their career and would use that information to build relationships, make the assignments more relevant, and assess the rigor for each pupil. Zany replied that he wished to be a professional gambler, and qualified his statement by saying he was already a professional poker player.

In the state of California there are plenty of card casinos, but usually these require patrons to be 21 years of age since alcohol is often served. Still, going to the right card room could easily make Zany's statement plausible. Zany volunteered that he even envisioned himself at an older age to be on the professional poker players' circuit and treated like the king of the high rollers by casinos all over the world. I really didn't want to crush his already enormous self-esteem, so I just nodded and moved on.

Speaking of moving on, Zany changed occupations fairly regularly. Zany told the class that he was hired by a pizza chain known for fast delivery, but he just worked there one night. Zany impressed his new boss by requesting more than a double extra-large sized number of pizzas to deliver on what was already a very busy night because the 49ers were playing. Zany delivered a few pizzas, kept the cash, and vanished off the grid with the rest of the pizzas for himself and some of his friends at an undisclosed location to party, perhaps play some poker, and enjoy the 49ers game. Zany bragged that he even charged his hungry friends for the pizza and never hinted that he had stolen the pizzas so he made double the cash. That was the last day he worked at that location as a pizza delivery person.

Zany pulled the same stunt at various restaurants by essentially stealing from the cash register in addition to absconding with generous quantities of food. Zany was not just interested in food service, although typical of teenaged boys he always complained that he was forever hungry. Zany enjoyed being employed at various large-scale discount stores where he was literally stealing everything in sight. Zany even took requests from fellow classmates for items they wanted like the latest limited edition shoes, designer hats, etc. which he said he would buy for them at a reduced price by using his employee discount. Of course, his employee discount was better known as the "five finger discount."

Zany was able to continue this scheme for a relatively long time at big box stores, which meant a few days or perhaps even a week or so. Zany laughed when on more than one occasion, a real customer, or even secret shopper, would ask for his directions to something that was close by, but he would send them to the other end of the store and hide in the break room.

At one very large brick-and-mortar outlet store, Zany was the only one on duty in his section, so he decided to talk about non-consequential items to a customer for just enough time so he wouldn't have to work with the crowds of people who were lining up desperately looking for his help. Those customers waiting in line were becoming more and more annoyed as Zany told jokes that were not funny, asked inappropriate questions, and voluntarily gave negative opinions about products for which he had absolutely no knowledge. When Zany could ultimately not drag out any more time, he walked away from the customers looking briefly at his wrist, smiled, and said he was now on break time. Zany explained to me that he needed to do this sort of thing because he had to hone his skills at bluffing customers in order to do well at the card tables so he considered his approach "On-the-job-training".

At grocery stores where he worked, his method of attack would be to work as a bagger or stocker, fill shopping carts with groceries and pretend to deliver the groceries to customers in the parking lot. Sometimes this would be to his fellow high school buddies who were more than anxious to load up on steaks, snacks, and beer for a very small price. Zany saw no problem with supplying anyone with any product, but the finer things did better for his wallet. Even before the managers could pick up on his game, Zany was long gone with the choicest of items for himself.

How did he land these jobs?

Because Zany had so much job experience, he knew exactly what to say to make a good impression on his bosses and weasel his way out of blame. Zany patently never admitted blame, even if he was caught in the act he would always deny, deny, deny and twist the conversation into something else. Zany's ego was the only reason that his activities came to light. For example, Zany was supercharged about the perks of working at a store which had furniture, and using the recliners, couches, and beds for relaxation while telling its customers and curious bystanders that he was working quality control, which necessitated them leaving him alone so he could get some effective data without data disrupting interruptions by outsiders. He must have had an amazing "poker-face" to convince people of that story!

In a large metropolitan area there are obviously many unwary restaurants, stores, warehouses, and opportunities for Zany to practice his skill set, but it didn't take long for Zany to eliminate numerous venues. Zany's antics eliminated a city directory-worth of establishments as targets of opportunity. Zany was only 18 years old but already many of his adventures started to catch up with him so his travel time on the 101Freeway to new opportunities increased slowly but surely, which diminished his profit margin. Zany volunteered that even at some more distant restaurants and stores he ran into managers from previous places where he had run amok and they were less than inviting to offer him employment.

I suggested to Zany that he might try to find a new place to work and do an honest day's work, build a good reputation with his boss, and perhaps see his salary increase or get promoted. Zany flatly rejected this idea. Zany was dead set on being a professional gambler. I think some of the card casinos began to get wise to him and ban Zany. Perhaps by visiting these gambling places so often they began to grind the money out of him so he was not really winning, or maybe, as incredulous to Zany as it might seem, there might be other professional gamblers who were far better.

I was relatively lucky to have Zany in my class because he did find math to be relatively important. I knew I did not have to worry about Zany's California Assessment of Student Performance and Progress (CAASPP) math scores, but other teachers were not so fortunate. Needless to say he counted cards and felt entirely justified when he tried to pull every trick imaginable at the card casinos, but he was fairly diligent in doing the math curriculum. Yes, like almost all students, Zany had an app on his phone which would do the math and show the work, but he was cognizant that his supposed unsurpassed mental mathematical abilities were essential because most casinos would not permit any form of electronics.

The cocky Zany was challenged by an angry girl who questioned him in a manner insuring everyone could hear in the classroom, "Aren't those big, fancy casinos built on the money lost by the foolish compulsive gamblers like you?"

Zany's response was quick and telling. "I don't go to the casinos to loose, I go to play cards only to win and win big, so it's not my money but yours, and all the other foolish amateurs that goes to build those casinos and keep me in my high roller lifestyle."

I wanted to keep a good relationship with Zany so I was apprehensive about calling his counselor or his parents, however, I couldn't quietly stand by any longer. The parents said he was 18 years old and could make his own decisions and if there were any concerns, it was none of my concern, nor the school's business. The parents threatened to hire an attorney to litigate a multimillion dollar case that would leave me penniless for defamation of their son. The counselor said she would consider making an appointment to explore issues with Zany but I should be aware that if my concerns were correct, the first step would have to be for Zany to admit he had a problem and seek help on his own, otherwise she would be just spinning her wheels with him. Besides, the counselor could only suggest and provide the opportunity for various directions to enable self-help. The counselor was cognizant of the problem but took the attitude of the "the emperor has no clothes" to protect herself and enjoy her own more pressing coffee and romance novel addiction.

I contented myself with the knowledge that it was only my job to teach math and not to overstep my boundaries, even though I could see this student was headed on a precarious path. Zany really liked math, probability and statistics so he was diligent in my classroom. At least he was not on opioids…

On campus fellow students teased him occasionally by mockingly suggesting self-help telephone hotlines from billboards or television, but Zany always had a comeback answer. Zany was their favorite guy for almost anything, so they were happy to see him do whatever he wanted with his funds. Only a handful of the students had the foresight to wonder what they would do without him next year, but they all figured he would always be in the neighborhood working a diverse buffet of jobs while offering his services to them at discount prices.-And eating well!

19 RAPUNZEL

The city of Chicago is made up of neighborhoods based on ethnic groups. Although it is now in legal and forbidden to discriminate on race, religion, or national origin, many sections of Chicago are predominantly one nationality, and that's just how the winds in our city blow.. Around the turn-of-the-century (1900) the city was an entry port for large numbers of European immigrants to the United States. Their communities often were centers of culture which quickly came to resemble the old countries from which the settlers came. Today if you know where to go it is possible to enjoy fantastic cuisine in various sections, so Chicago is kind of like a giant smorgasbord of culinary delights from around the globe.

In the mid-1940s new immigrants came from Mexico, but lately, while I am teaching English as a Second Language (ESL), sometimes referred to as English to Speakers of Other Languages (ESOL) or English Language

Learning (ELL), we are receiving large numbers of students from Africa, Southwest Asia, South Asia, and East Asia. We still get some occasional Eastern Europeans and Latin American students, but not in the numbers that we used to see in the old days. Another surprising facet is that we have discovered the students are much more intelligent and sometimes better educated than our native students.

Really my job is to try to help kids make their dreams come true, just like the goal of all teachers. Although the paperwork is a nightmare, the satisfaction of seeing students become proficient in a foreign language more than makes up for the hassle of mindless paperwork and regulations. Unlike the special education kids, we rarely have lawnmower/helicopter parents hovering with lawyers to mow us down with lawsuits so we can teach to the best of our ability and enjoy the satisfaction of seeing gratitude for our efforts from their parents. Occasionally some of the English language learners had their feelings hurt when they noticed that their classrooms were adjacent to the special education classrooms which inferred that they were sometimes considered less gifted, but that's another story. I think Rapunzel said it best when she disgustedly exclaimed "We don't want to be associated with the crayon-eaters."

A sad commentary on my city is that many of these students have fled violence just to arrive in a city that is as dangerous as the war-torn country they left, and because they are not Americanized they are often unknowingly make mis-steps resulting in them becoming unsuspecting victims. I always taught American culture along with the language for the aforementioned reason.

In the section of Chicago where I teach, it is a predominantly Mexican neighborhood. English is clearly taking over, so that almost everyone speaks English except the original settlers who are now grandparents or great-grandparents. Still you can see signs in both languages and just like every other neighborhood in my city the cultural traditions continue with an American twist, so these children in the neighborhood are growing up in an area that's not really Mexico nor is it really the United States, it's a place somewhere in between and unique.

Rapunzel came to my school directly from Mexico, where she came from a very traditional household. She had her hair and long braids with colorful pieces of cloth woven into the braids and the coordinating cloth would change to suit her clothing, which was often a long dress. It must've been a long and tedious process to decorate her long locks of hair which reached down below her waist. I felt very sad for Rapunzel because she had very few friends. Even the other Hispanic children in the school could not speak Spanish so they were of little help, and I got the feeling that they made fun of her. One time I saw a Rapunzel get angry when someone said something to her in Spanish that she didn't like so she started swinging her hair like a weed- wacker thereby smacking the other student in the face from a distance with her hair.

English language learners will often have difficulty with drama and poetry, but certain slang terms can also be very difficult to know when to use. I tried not to laugh when a puzzled Rapunzel matter-of-factly said "What the F** are you talking about mister?".

"Where is Chris Pratt when you need him" was another

one of her statements that almost made me blush, but my favorite was "Johnny was indicted for what he did with the apple seeds."

Did she know what she was saying? Was she learning English well enough to be able to use double entendre? Did someone in the school use these phrases and encourage her to repeat them?

It is a Mexican custom for 15-year-old girls, to have a "Quinceanera". It's possible to look and find a number of answers for what this celebration of a Mexican female reaching 15 years of age really is, but in Chicago it amounted to one of three things: a big party, a car, or a fantastic trip. Giving a 15-year-old girl a car in Chicago is tantamount to giving someone a loaded gun, so very few of the families would encourage that sort of choice. The trip idea was also somewhat negatively viewed, but it was more common than the car. Typically the trip would involve taking the girl to Mexico to visit family although a visit to the Disney parks was a highly desired close second. The number one choice was a party and for Rapunzel who had just come from Mexico you can guess that's what her parents wanted her to do and she obediently complied.

Chicago was neither here nor there, so the Quinceanera custom was adopted by many other Hispanic immigrants from places like El Salvador, Puerto Rico, etc. If you think about how many 15-year-old Hispanic females there are in a city the size of Chicago it is easy to imagine that there's more than one Quinceanera every weekend in the neighborhood where my school is located and the competitive spirit among 15 year old girls is fierce, so these parties became a giant business and took on a life of their own.

The father and mother thank people for coming to their party even if they didn't invite them just because it is a sign of respect and gratitude in the highly competitive market of where people have the option to select a plethora of grand blowout parties every weekend. One student's father told me proudly that he was going to spend more on his daughter at this time of her life than at her future wedding, because at this time he did not have to share her with another man. As a teacher I was often invited and would try to attend briefly every one of these parties that I possibly could in order to build rapport the students and their families, but also because the parties were just plain old fun.

The Quinceanera usually included a number of young boys dressed either in tuxedo or traditional outfits who would dance and serenade the girl for her 15th birthday party. There were even crews of professional adolescent boys who would do this to earn money. Some of these boys could sing in Spanish but did know word they were singing, but just reacted to the crowd so they would know when to smile or flirt. Occasionally the songs were the latest in a Spanish form of Rap and Hip Hop called "Reggaeton" that not even the native speakers knew what was being said in Spanish and/or English, which really led to some wild dancing. Perhaps for the Reggeaton songs it was good the parents did not know what the lyrics meant, but from the teen's reactions and gyrations to the songs' lyrics I suspect it was not good clean fun.

These parties were full of drama and alcohol, which often go hand-in-hand. Just like the movie "Wedding Crashers", there were probably many people at these parties who were professional crashers. Plenty of the students at the high school knew they could go to any and all of these parties and get plastered drunk, as well as eat like kings for free. It almost became a weekly contest to see who could have the wildest party and impress the other 15-year-olds, as well as their parents and extended families. Sometimes I thought the freshman kids did so much drinking each weekend that they were sure to be in a 12 step program by the time they were sophomores. As things went from bad to worse in Chicago in terms of violence, the parties were often crashed by groups of thugs intent on stealing and shooting to the point that it was almost an expected ritual of the event just like the doll, high heels, and makeup for the 15 year-old girl.

Rapunzel was dressed in what looked like a junior version of a white wedding dress, and was given high-heeled shoes and a beautiful designer doll. The doll reminded me of the ones in a particular store in Chicago frequented by female executives where outrageously expensive and exquisite dolls are sold to add to their doll collections. The doll represented the last all of childhood, while the high-heeled shoes represented womanhood. All of these items were extremely fancy and expensive, so sometimes friends and family would be asked to provide these items and get the spotlight by making the presentation to the girl during the event. This was often a very coveted position which only added to the drama and excitement.

At one of these parties some of the fellas went into the lavatory and caught the quarterback stone drunk and apparently misbehaving with one of the towel boys for the cheerleading squad. The quarterback, of course according to cliché, just so happened to be dating the head cheerleader, so within seconds there was hysterics of epic proportions. The head cheerleader insisted that everyone got it wrong and that her handsome boyfriend was drunk and sickly taken advantage of. The quarterback was embarrassed and so drunk and or high that he wasn't making much sense. The towel boy was an Asian student of mine was always very quiet and diligent in his studies, so he said nothing and vanished. I wasn't even present for any of this melee so my account comes from bits and pieces of gossip that I really did not want to hear. How was I connected to this? Well, I made the 911 call from my other job.

Like many teachers I worked a second job in order to make ends meet. In fact my job was working nights at a hot dog shop, so meat helped ends meet. I was busy serving some of the students from the high school when we think the quarterback's car came speeding down the city street at high velocity. Apparently the head cheerleader was driving, but we can't say for certain, because the car was traveling so fast. Again, according to rumor, the wasted boyfriend was in the passenger seat and apparently confessed to the indignant cheerleader that he did not know who he loved more; the head cheerleader, or the towel boy, or maybe both. At that point the irate head cheerleader, allegedly in a fit of jealous rage, knocked him out of the speeding car and on to the road then sped off in a blaze of indignation. I really can't say that, because all I glimpsed, and all the crowd witnessed, was our head quarterback fly out onto the street and get badly bruised in a split second event that seemed like an eternity leaving the entire restaurant in a state of suspended animation before several adults got up from their seats and ran to the street to try to pull him from the middle of the busy road in order to avoid him being run over.. Cellular telephones were working at warp speed as rumors and gossip spread like a wildfire and burned up the city faster than old lady O'Leary's cow. The broken bones and other injuries sustained by the quarterback were explained as football injuries from the game and his lack of coherence was naturally due to concussion suffered on the playing field. The cheerleader announced she had broken up with the quarterback because he was not on the team and the towel boy was just laundered out of the cheerleader system.

At every school there's a social hierarchy, so with the head cheerleader suddenly available students began to break up at a frenzied pace in order to socially move-up. I witnessed the mad scramble, which resembled a shark feeding frenzy, both at school and countless awkward first dates at the hot dog stand. By the way, I really liked working at the restaurant, but the puns were the wurst.

I got my German Shepherd Duke from an ex-girlfriend. She got me the stray dog as a surprise for my birthday because she thought the dog would bring us together and perhaps be like a training wheel for the future kids that we might make. All of a sudden, one day she split in it was just Duke and I, so the stray dog was more loyal than that B---- ----.

German shepherds are great dogs to have. Late at night when I had to go to the corner store to get my cigarettes, Duke was my faithful companion and no one would mess with me. Duke was also good to have at the local parks in order to attract the ladies, because he was kind of my wing man but since he didn't say anything I didn't have to worry about any slipups or embarrassing comments, like when going out with the guys. It was also nice to go to the parks and get some fresh air, plus the walks were great exercise and a chance to smoke.

Eventually a new girlfriend came along and moved in with us. One night when I got home from work selling links, Duke was all out of sorts. It was hard to figure out what was wrong with Duke, but something was definitely awry. Then I noticed all but one of my girlfriend's birth-control pills had been eaten and it didn't take long to figure out the bite marks were from Duke. No wonder Duke was so all out of sorts and was starting to act like a duchess. Off to the veterinarian we went, and Duke had his stomach pumped. This was the worst possible night for something like that to happen, because the next day's lesson was about not confusing the past form with the past participle of irregular verbs which is a daunting task for people learning English.

Some other difficult things to explain to English language learners which even native English speakers confuse:
How are you?

I'm doing well?
Or
I'm doing good?

Or as Rapunzel had learned from her acquaintances in the halls when asked to practice what she had learned "What's it F—ing to ya".

While sitting in the room waiting anxiously for some good news about Duke, I saw a Rapunzel and the cheerleader both working behind the desk. Rapunzel was extremely happy to see me and said she would make sure that my Duke was treated like a king. The gratitude shown by Rapunzel is one of the perks of being a teacher and I'm sure Duke appreciated it. Seeing the cheerleader work with Rapunzel also put my mind at ease about where Rapunzel was truly learning conversational English...

20 THE BASKETBALL JONES

"The most successful student that I ever had was the one
whose life I had the least impact."

In the city of New York basketball is king. Any kid with
a pair of shoes can find a group and a basketball within
easy reach nearly anywhere in the city. From childhood
pickup games to a senior citizens' league, the game is
played everywhere and by almost everybody. Sure there are
other sports, but in the city there is not much room for
sports that require large amounts of space like football and
baseball, and just too many youngsters that unfortunately
cannot afford all the specialized equipment necessary for
other sports.

Ask any kid in the city who the top basketball players
are and they can both name them and argue to defend their
position, but even the adults would have a hard time telling
you the mayor's cabinet. These are just the facts that

everybody knows but no one wants to say. My job as head basketball coach in the highly competitive high school arena was to make sure our teams had a great record, the players got a good education, and the kids stayed out of trouble.

The Basketball Jones could dribble with his fingers, toes and nose. He was absolutely incredible. He played club ball, street ball, and high school ball. In club ball Basketball Jones really made his mark. Recruiters were constantly unofficially watching him everywhere, but were very careful to follow NCAA guidelines when visiting the high school. This is just the way it is when colleges get the whiff of the scent of the next Michael Jordan, LeBron James, Stephen Curry, etc. Some of my scouting friends even lamented that this boy was so good they were afraid to invest much in him for fear that he would turn pro too quickly and they'd only be able to get a season from him. The Basketball Jones was being badgered by so many people that he just stopped listening to anyone except his mother, so the game became how to influence dear old mom.

The Basketball Jones's mother was a single mom with multiple children living in a rent control apartment. Her son was probably the best thing that ever happened in her life because he was going to be her meal ticket. All the recruiters knew the way to get to the Basketball Jones was through his mother, so they concentrated on her in order to get her son to sign with their school, but some of the more unscrupulous recruiters targeted the money-hungry girlfriends. It was a very fine line that the recruiters had to walk in order not to violate NCAA statutes which would assuredly be scrutinized closely due to the value of this soon to be great basketball player.

Quick question: Who needs a Sport Utility Vehicle (SUV) if they live in NYC?

The recruiters were not the only ones who could smell success. Every little girl at the high school threw themselves at him in order for him to be their baby's daddy. The millions he would make with a pro contract and potential of everything from tennis shoes to reality television shows put dollar signs in the eyes of every female who came close to him. As his coach I instructed him to keep his head in the game, get good grades, stay out of trouble, and not be too distracted by all the ladies who were so desirous of his attentions.

To make matters worse for the team, and add to my consternation, he stopped showing up for practice in order to hang out with the throng of thongs who craved all of his time. Countless scuffles between females erupted on campus because they all claimed him as their territory and stealing lovers was just as legal to them as stealing balls in basketball. Each one of these girls was anxious to claim their winning lotto ticket by getting pregnant. Basketball Jones should've been concerned with travelling to a good college team and helping our team win, but his mind and body were off court.

Hamlet was a friend and teammate who fed the ball to Basketball Jones. One day Hamlet came to me before practice and said he must quit the team. How could this enthusiastic player suddenly quit? Did Hamlet loose his mind? Something rotten had occurred but what?

Hamlet revealed that his mother just gave birth so she needed him to be a babysitter for his new half-brother. Probably a felony, and certainly more than trifling for Hamlet, the baby's daddy was his ex-pal Basketball Jones.

If it had been anybody else, the moment a player misses a practice without an excuse, that player is benched for the following game. This probably would've been the best medicine for his head, but he was allowed to play. Even on a team full of talent, Basketball Jones was so good that he dominated the court. I really didn't have to come up with much in the way of strategy other than give the ball to Basketball Jones. The other players resented deeply that they had to go to practice and go through the motions but the Basketball Jones didn't have to play by the same rules.

Literally our squad was a one-man team and we were winning big-time in the Big Apple. Probably every coach in the city knew what was going on but kept silent. Basketball Jones even had the local TV stations covering his play, sometimes giving him more airtime than the NBA pros. I knew exactly what to say to the media folks, but they didn't want to talk to me.

One of his disgruntled teammates, I think it was Hamlet, was asked by a sports reporter what it was like to play on the team with the Basketball Jones and he replied " Don't ask me. I don't play _with_ Basketball Jones, I play _for_ him."

As expected the pregnancy rate at the high school skyrocketed, we probably could have made it on a special edition of the national news for the exponential teen pregnancy rate and have a number of community leaders come to discuss reasons for the pandemic, but the real culprit was Basketball Jones who seemed to be in a competition with some Saudi Arabian princes to see who could have the biggest harem and father the most children.

In the locker room we had some inspirational slogans painted on the wall. There was one slogan that related to getting a good education in order to be successful in life because a strong body and a strong mind are the keys to success. Basketball Jones certainly had the body, and we made sure we had a troop of very attractive and talented female students who would tutor Basketball Jones so he could pass all of his classes with flying colors, but his off-court judgment needed some work. As his coach there really wasn't anything in basketball, or anything else that I could teach him, or that he would even bother to listen, but I tried.

The U.S. Department of Education's Office for Civil Rights (OCR) enforces, among other statutes, Title IX of the Education Amendments of 1972. Title IX protects people from discrimination based on sex in education programs or activities that receive Federal financial assistance. Title IX states that:

No person in the United States shall, on the basis of sex, be excluded from participation in, be denied the benefits of, or be subjected to discrimination under any education program or activity receiving Federal financial assistance.

So when "Angela the Angel" showed up after school to fill position as a manager for the basketball team, the potential ramifications with the propensities of Basketball Jones was the first thing that came to my mind, but I also remembered Title IX, so, ever the pragmatist, I had to say, "Yes".

Angela the Angel was the best thing that ever happened to our team. She told me she wanted to be the first female head coach in the NBA and she recognized she did not have the physical ability to play in the game, but basketball was her life. Angela the Angel was early to practice and the last one to leave. Angela the Angel was always smiling and happy while strategically surmising and suggesting what would be the best strategies for our team. Angela the Angel was so keen on basketball strategies that her second set of eyes caught things I missed, so she was a super asset to the team and I. Angela the Angel, thankfully, professed no personal interest in Basketball Jones, which relieved my initial apprehension. Angela the Angel did, however, have to convince a large number of hostile campus females of her altruistic goals, but she was up to the task.

Everybody had to draw out strategies on poster paper that we would hang in the locker room and use as quick visual representations during halftime to help our players understand what they needed to do in order to be successful. In education we categorize learning as either audio, visual, or kinesthetic. No person is 100% in any one of these three categories, and although most of my basketball players were predominantly kinesthetic learners, having a visual often helped some of the players comprehend what they needed to do. Although these drawings only needed to be drawn as simple X's and O's on a Basketball Court template, Angela the Angel put her heart and soul into creating an artistic masterpiece which served as an inspiration for other students. In fact it was one of the boys on the team that came up with the nickname "the Angel".

There was a young administrator who had a very different nickname, because although his name was Jonathan Ashe everyone referred to him as "Jack" Ashe. Jack was the kind of guy who really was an awful teacher and was not into education because he liked kids or teaching. Jack was in education because he wanted to be a the next NYC Department of Education Superintendent. His skill was finding good teachers and tweaking their work so he could claim credit and advance his career. Jack knew every buzzword in education and could spin them to stupefy others and justify his calculated career climbing decisions. Jonathan Ashe thought he was wicked smart for taking credit for the work of others, but once anyone dealt with the real Jack Ashe, it was obvious to even the weakest of minds that Jack had padded his resume, however, by that time it was too late to do anything about it.

Jack gave a series of mandates but increasing noticed a lackluster campus compliance. Because Jack did not support those who followed his directives, Jack had lost the staff's confidence, but continued to add exaggerated results to his resume, which made some say "The Emperor has no clothes"…

When Jack came into the coaches' office he referred to the posters in the locker room and asked me if I wanted to be a coach or an art teacher. The alarm bells started to ring, but I went ahead and asked him why he had such a question because the basketball team was poised to take the city championship which was tantamount to saying we would be state champions. The glimmer in Jack's eye when he visualized his school would be state basketball champions and he could add the accolade to his resume was probably the real reason for Jack's visit.

Jack admonished me for using paper to make posters and explained the kids could do all of that very easily electronically on their phones. When I explained to him the kids would not be carrying their phones while playing basketball, cell phone reception in the locker room was extremely poor, and posters would help visual learners, he threatened to have me arrested for misuse of state funding for paper, as well as fired for insubordination.

Jack went on to call me "Coach Flintstone" for using such ancient technology and insinuated that he might need to look for a better coach because having kids color with markers was far beneath the dignity of students in this century.

Jack degraded me further by saying that we didn't teach kids how to add, subtract, multiply, or divide, anymore because that could be done with a calculator or phone so those skills were no longer consequential in our modern lives, just like we didn't teach kids how to use flint and steel to start fires to cook now that we have microwave ovens. I got the point, but he made it excruciating by listing even more examples like why we don't have kids make maps in geography classes now that Google maps can tell us locations within seconds.

I often thought what it would be like to go to the state high court in Albany with the union's fleet of lawyers by my side and see Jack Ashe squirm. Would the New York Post manage to put him on their front page and we see his career path go up in flames?

My main concern, however, was having enough time to do all of the necessary chores needed to keep our team going, rather than be caught up in Jack Ashe's time wasting shenanigans, so the posters were removed. I even signed a document which was put in my file to document that I understood and would comply with this directive without complaint. Besides the whole magic of the strategy, was in essence, to give the ball to Basketball Jones and he would do the rest.

A combination of city and state taxes for cigarettes in New York City is approximately $5.85 per pack making cigarettes over $13 for a pack of 20. The idea is to make cigarettes so expensive that no one can afford to smoke. The unintended consequence in the city is smoking has become very desirable because it shows status that a person can afford to smoke, and when someone goes to a smoking area the mob is always there to provide cheap cigarettes bought elsewhere and imported which has led the city to spend millions to crack down on purveyors of illegal cigarettes. Some of the less wealthy students and/or those students who wanted a thrill were routinely recruited by the mob to drive to Virginia to buy cigarettes in large quantities for about $10 less per pack, which was entirely legal and bring them to a location near the city for distribution in the booming illicit cigarette trade. Angela the Angel got caught up in this illicit business. Angela the Angel had big dreams about her future but her parents had little money and it was unlikely that she would ever get any kind of scholarship, so while Basketball Jones was living the high life for his skills in basketball, after games Angela the Angel was living the high speed life with weekend trips to Virginia to keep her dreams on the fast track. A few jolts of espresso, followed by turning the high beams on, and putting the pedal to the metal once outside the city, was the typical method for the drivers. There were even some folks in the city who wanted to save time and money on hotels that would drive like this all the way to their vacation destinations in Florida.

Hard to say whether lack of sleep, or lack of caffeine, or even lack of driving experience, drove Angela the Angel into one of the pylons of an overpass on I-95. The casket was closed at her funeral, but we had all the members of the team come to pay their respects. This is when one of the members of the team expressed his feeling that Angela was a beautiful angel that we did not recognize until she was gone. Before the funeral I drew a large A+ on the exquisite basketball strategy poster which Angela the Angel made and subsequently Mr. Jack Ashe had me remove that I presented to her parents, whom framed it in their apartment. I guess all the electronic stuff that she submitted for her classes couldn't really be framed but the poster could be framed and it reminded her parents of the awesome daughter that God had given to them.

It came as an ironic surprise when Basketball Jones returned to our campus to have his picture taken in the locker room with those old inspirational slogans for an NBA documentary about the latest basketball sensation to sweep the nation, because he was rarely present in the locker room during his entire stint on our team.

Basketball Jones had his pick of colleges, and true to form, he turned pro and was signed to an amazing NBA contract. Unfortunately for him he needed a fleet of attorneys who gobbled up almost all of his money fighting against paternity suits. Product endorsements started to drop off as his reputation as an off court player and rumors of abuse soured potential advertisers, but Basketball Jones was still courted by a number of female celebrities who got bit parts for him in Hollywood productions. Thanks to his temporary lady friends., Basketball Jones even managed the trifecta of being on the sports channels, the entertainment channels, and the national news, for all of the mind-boggling activities full court pressing around him

Trash talking in basketball is a part of the game, and most players learn to deal with it. A little good banter makes the game exciting and shows the enthusiasm for the players, so the Basketball Jones was well acquainted with this atmosphere, which just made it harder for him to comprehend that his life had been spinning out of control because he would listen to no one. During free throws, the other side's fans would shout "Indiana" and "Temple of Doom", but eventually switched to "Child Support".

Having babies' mamas show up at the games to heckle made him infamous, so his star faltered fast, and he quickly became the epitome of everything that was wrong with pro sports becoming a negative example of what an athlete should be. The money he was hemorrhaging every time he walked the street vanished.

We saw each other out of peripheral vision once at a mall in Jersey, but we both pretended we didn't know each other.

Really, this high school basketball coach had no impact on the life of the Basketball Jones, and neither did Mr. Jack Ashe, even if the success of championship team was on Jack Ashe's fugazzi resume...

ABOUT THE AUTHOR

Civil War Historian whose works include: "Confederate Cannoneers, Infantry, and Cavalry Can a Clad: The Sinking of the USS Eastport" *Civil War News* XLIV No. 5 (May 2018), 22-24. "Foiled Federal February Fandangos: How Southern Soldiers Saved Their South Texas Sweethearts from Unsolicited Salutations" *UDC Magazine* LXXVII No. 11 (December 2014) 19-22. Consultant for *The Civil War Letters of Louis Lehmann* (Hill College Press) 2011 and appearance as an actor in Last of the Mohicans. This is the author's first work of fiction.

Married in Franklin, Robertson County, Texas and father of four, who enjoys reading, writing, and Latin Dance, especially Salsa. He is fluent in Spanish and has extensive travel experience in Europe, Mexico, and the USA.

Made in the USA
Monee, IL
03 August 2021